101 GREAT
WARSHIPS

101 GREAT WARSHIPS

LEGENDARY WARSHIPS FROM WWI TO THE PRESENT

Robert Jackson

Sandcastle Books

This edition published in 2008 by
Sandcastle Books Ltd
The Stables
Sheriffs Lench Court
Sheriffs Lench
Worcestershire
WR11 4SN
United Kingdom

M 10 9 8 7 6 5 4 3 2 1

ISBN-13: 978-1-906020-53-8

Editorial and design by
Amber Books Ltd
Bradley's Close
74–77 White Lion Street
London N1 9PF
United Kingdom
www.amberbooks.co.uk

Project Editor: Sarah Uttridge
Design: Graham Curd
Picture Research: Terry Forshaw and Kate Green

Picture credits
All photographs courtesy of **Cody Images** except for the following:
Art-Tech/Aerospace: 7, 32, 37-41, 47, 55, 61, 63, 65, 67, 73, 90, 92, 95-98
Art-Tech/MARS: 20, 27, 29, 33, 36, 46, 54, 64, 69, 70, 72, 76-78, 80, 82, 83;
BAE Systems: 109; De Agostini: 18, 25; Popperfoto: 13, 24, 49, 74; Thales: 110;
U.S. Department of Defense: 8, 9, 88, 94, 99-101, 103, 105, 106, 108
All artworks courtesy of **De Agostini** except for the following: **Art-Tech/Aerospace:** 13, 24, 25, 28, 31-33, 37, 40, 50, 52, 61, 63, 65, 72, 94, 101; **Mark Franklin:** 103, 107-110
Bob Garwood: 60, 83; **Mainline Design:** 43, 102

Printed in China

Contents

Introduction

In 1906 the British launched HMS *Dreadnought*, a ship which combined every single technical advance to date, from new steam turbine engines to electrically controlled gun turrets. *Dreadnought* made every other battleship obsolete, including those in her own navy, and gave her name to an entirely new class of warship.

However, *Dreadnought's* time as the world's number one did not last very long. By 1908 the Royal Navy was building so-called 'Super-Dreadnoughts', which were more than 8128 tonnes (8000 tons) heavier. The future of the capital ship seemed to lie in bigger and bigger battleships carrying guns of ever-increasing size. But questions were now being asked as to the battleship's future. Many were wondering exactly how useful in battle these huge floating gun batteries would be. Countries such as Germany were ceding the battleship contest and were beginning to develop other warship types such as battle cruisers, which were designed for fast commerce raiding rather than naval battles. More ominously, Germany was also investing in a fleet of torpedo-carrying submarines. During World War II, the U-boat war in the battle of the Atlantic would devastate the Allied convoys until 1943, when submarine detection equipment became sufficiently developed.

It was to be the aircraft, though, which would ultimately make the battleship redundant. In the area of naval air warfare the Royal Navy led the field, with aircraft carriers already operational by the time World War I ended. There was a new offensive weapon in the naval arsenal, but throughout the 1920s and 1930s traditionalists still remained convinced that any future naval warfare would be decided by battleships.

The Royal Navy's Type 42 destroyer was a good design, but suffered from financial constraints that restricted its protection and performance.

At the beginning of World War II, battleships such as *Haruna* of Japan and the Royal Navy's HMS *Nelson* still represented the most powerful war machines made by man. But by 1942 the type had been completely eclipsed by a new kind of warfare. The attacks by torpedo aircraft on Taranto and Pearl Harbor and the sinking of *Repulse* and *Prince of Wales* off Malaya proved that a battleship could not exist without control of the air space above it. The age of the aircraft carrier had arrived. In the Cold War the threat to land-based bombers forced both sides to develop nuclear-powered ballistic missile submarines capable of long patrols and virtually undetectable. However, it is the US Navy's carrier battle group that now represents the apogee of modern naval power. And yet the carriers require substantial naval assets to protect them from both air and submarine attack: guided-missile cruisers, guided-missile destroyers, anti-submarine warfare destroyers, anti-submarine warfare frigates and even one or two nuclear submarines – proof that a capital ship, no matter how powerful, is always vulnerable, and that all ships are dependent on each other.

The guided missile destroyer *Arleigh Burke* travelling at speed. This vessel is designed to operate in any warfare environment.

The assault ship HMS *Ocean* was designed specifically to undertake and support amphibious and helicopter-borne landings.

Erzherzog Karl

Forming part of the Austrian Navy's 3rd Division during World War I, the *Erzherzog Karl* had an undistinguished war career in the Adriatic.

COUNTRY: Austria
TYPE: Battleship
LAUNCH DATE: 14 October 1903
CREW: 700
DISPLACEMENT: 10,640 tonnes (10,472 tons)
DIMENSIONS: 126.2m x 21.7m x 7.5m (414ft 2in x 71ft 6in x 24ft 8in)
RANGE: 7412km (4000nm) at 10 knots
ARMAMENT: 12 190mm (7.5in), four 240mm (9.45in) guns
POWERPLANT: Twin screw, triple expansion engines
PERFORMANCE: 20.5 knots

The *Erzherzog Karl* was a good ship for her size, but was obsolescent by the time she was completed in 1906–10.

Erzherzog Karl was named after Archduke Charles, Duke of Teschen (1771–1847), field marshal and commander of the Austrian forces against Napoleon. She was one of three units that formed the last of the pre-dreadnought type built for the Austrian Navy. She served in the Adriatic during World War I, where the naval war opened with large-scale fleet operations. Immediately after the outbreak of hostilities the entire Austrian battle fleet went south to escort the German Mediterranean Squadron to Pola, but its commander decided to make for Constantinople.

Erzherzog Karl was taken over by the newly created nation of Yugoslavia in 1919. However, in 1920 she was handed over to France as part of Austria's war preparations and subsequently scrapped.

Electrically powered turrets

She is known for being the first warship to have her secondary guns housed in electrically powered turrets. Her sister ships, *Erzherzog Ferdinand Max* and *Erzherzog Friedrich*, were good vessels for their size but obsolescent by the time they were completed in 1906–10.

While being towed to Toulon in 1920, *Erzherzog Karl* went aground at Bizerte, Tunisia, and was broken up on the spot.

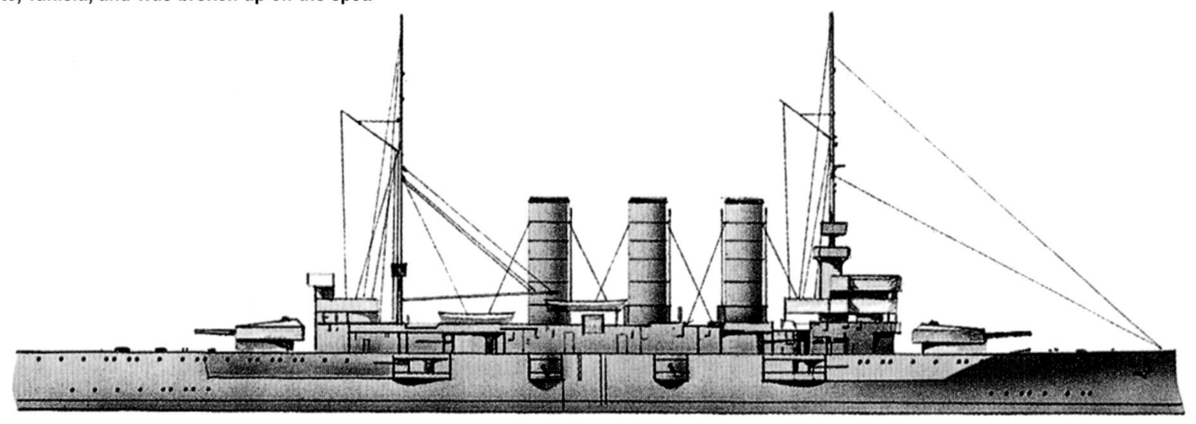

C-Class Submarines

The C-class submarines were designed mainly for service in coastal waters around the British Isles, but they ended by going much farther afield, for example, to Russia.

COUNTRY: Great Britain
TYPE: Attack submarine
LAUNCH DATE: 1906
CREW: 16
DISPLACEMENT: Surfaced: 295 tonnes (290 tons), submerged: 325 tonnes (320 tons)
DIMENSIONS: 43m x 4m x 3.5m (141ft x 13ft 1in x 11ft 4in)
SURFACE RANGE: 2414km (1431nm) at 8 knots
ARMAMENT: Two 457mm (18in) torpedo tubes
POWERPLANT: Single screw petrol engine, one electric motor
PERFORMANCE: Surfaced: 12 knots, submerged: 7.5 knots

The Royal Navy's C-class submarines took part in some notable and courageous operations during World War I.

In 1906, having amassed considerable experience in submarine construction, the British Admiralty felt confident embarked on a fairly large production run with a new design, the C class. The decision to build a large number of these coastal boats was unwise, as it diverted precious resources from the construction of overseas patrol submarines. But, despite their use of petrol engines, cramped conditions and lack of endurance, they remained in service throughout the war, and crews liked them.

Epic submarine voyage

In 1910, by which time 37 were in service, three of them, escorted by the sloop *Rosario*, were towed to the Far East to join the China Squadron at Hong Kong, at the time a truly epic voyage for submarines; three more went to Gibraltar. During World War I four C-class boats were sent to Russia, but were scuttled to prevent them falling into German hands in the Baltic. C3 made a dramatic exit; on 23 April 1918, filled with high explosive and, commanded by Lt Richard D. Sandford, she crept into Zeebrugge harbour and was exploded under a steel viaduct as part of the British blocking operation there. The two officers and four men aboard were picked up, although wounded; Sandford was awarded the Victoria Cross.

The C-class boats were generally similar in appearance to the B class. Some were camouflaged later in the war.

Dreadnought

The appearance of the *Dreadnought* in 1906 changed the face of naval warfare, but began an arms race with Germany in the years leading up to World War I.

The appearance of HMS *Dreadnought* revolutionized the concept of battleship design, and brought a new dimension to war at sea.

COUNTRY: Great Britain
TYPE: Battleship
LAUNCH DATE: 10 February 1906
CREW: 695–773
DISPLACEMENT: 22,194 tonnes (21,845 tons)
DIMENSIONS: 160.4m x 25m x 8m (526ft 3in x 82ft x 26ft 3in)
RANGE: 11,916km (6620nm) at 10 knots
ARMAMENT: 10 304mm (12in) guns
POWERPLANT: Quadruple screw turbines
PERFORMANCE: 21.6 knots

The concept of the *Dreadnought* originated with Admiral Sir John Fisher, who was appointed First Sea Lord in 1904. An exponent of gunnery, he harboured a long-standing ambition to improve the Royal Navy's standard of shooting. During his time in command of the British Mediterranean Fleet he had demonstrated that engagements were feasible at ranges up to 5484m (6000yds) and that modern guns could achieve a good hit rate at up to 7312m (8000yds), provided they were deliberately aimed and that full salvoes were fired. When he became First Sea Lord he appointed a committee to design a battleship armed with the maximum number of 305mm (12in) guns. The result was HMS *Dreadnought*.

Advanced era of warship construction

With the launching of Dreadnought in 1906, a new and more advanced era of warship construction began. Dreadnought was the first 'all-big-gun' battleship, so much so that she made all existing battleships obsolete. Dreadnought saw active service in World War I, being surpassed only by even larger ships of her type, to which she gave her generic name. Despite her warlike reputation, during World War I she only sank one enemy vessel, a German submarine which she rammed. The Royal Navy's Dreadnought fleet at the outbreak of World War I was thinly stretched, and after two months of hostilities ships had to be sent to their home ports on the south coast for refit. This meant that two or three of the Grand Fleet's most important vessels were absent from active duty at any one time. She was scrapped in 1923.

HMS *Dreadnought* was the first battleship to feature a main armament of a single calibre. She served with the Grand Fleet until 1916.

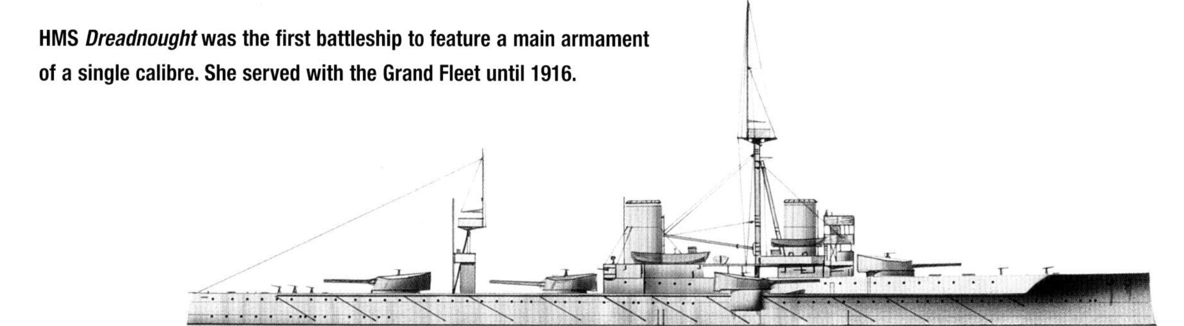

Invincible

The battlecruiser, like the dreadnought battleship, was a revolutionary concept for its time, but its role required it to sacrifice armour for speed, which proved to be its undoing.

COUNTRY: Great Britain	
TYPE: Battlecruiser	
LAUNCH DATE: 13 April 1907	
CREW: 784	
DISPLACEMENT: 20,421 tonnes (20,100 tons)	
DIMENSIONS: 175.5m x 23.9m x 7.7m (576ft x 78.5ft x 25.5ft)	
RANGE: 5559km (3000nm) at 25 knots	
ARMAMENT: Eight 305mm (12in), 16 102mm (4in) guns	
POWERPLANT: Four shaft geared turbines	
PERFORMANCE: 25 knots	

Lightly armoured at first, battlecruisers such as HMS *Invincible* became better protected as time went by.

The battlecruiser was a vessel nearly equal in armament to the new battleships but swifter. It could cruise ahead and scout for the main battle fleet, and be capable of overwhelming any conventional cruiser. In fact, the concept arose from the simple fact that existing armoured cruisers had evolved into ships so large and expensive that they had reached the end of their development potential. With a reduced armament, and protection sacrificed for speed, the battlecruisers were inevitably more vulnerable, as events at Jutland were to show in a tragic manner. Completed in 1908, *Invincible* was the world's first battlecruiser, and so was the first of an entirely new type of warship. It sacrificed armoured protection for speed, range and battleship-sized armament, and could outrun and outfight its prey – the armoured cruiser. However, as the disastrous loss of *Invincible* and two other battlecruisers at Jutland was to show, when up against a battleship's firepower, the lack of armour, particularly around the magazines, was a fatal flaw. Despite being refitted with more armour as a result of this débâcle, the vessel was deemed obsolete and development was stopped.

1026 lives lost

Invincible blew up and sank with the loss of 1026 lives, including Rear-Admiral H.L.A. Hood. The battlecruiser *Queen Mary* suffered the same fate at Jutland, exploding with the loss of 1266 lives after a direct hit from the battlecruiser *Derfflinger*.

Invincible's sister ships were the _Indomitable_ and _Inflexible_, displacing 15,527 tonnes (17,250 tons) each and carrying a complement of 784.

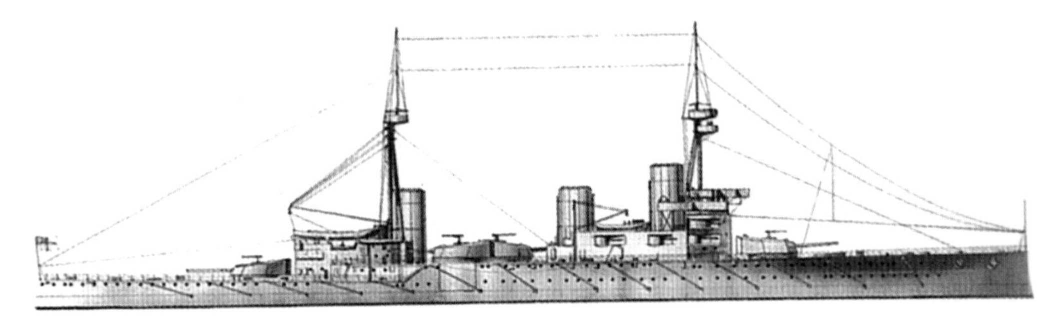

Ben-my-Chree

The conversion of the *Ben-my-Chree* to carry seaplanes was a bold step forward in the development of naval aviation. By the time she entered service, however, dedicated aircraft carriers were already on the horizon.

COUNTRY: Great Britain
TYPE: Seaplane carrier
LAUNCH DATE: 23 March 1908
CREW: 250
DISPLACEMENT: 3942 tonnes (3880 tons)
DIMENSIONS: 114m x 14m x 5.3m (375ft x 46ft x 17ft 6in)
RANGE: 2223km (1200nm) at 10 knots
ARMAMENT: Four, Short 184 seaplanes
POWERPLANT: Twin screw turbines
PERFORMANCE: 24.5 knots

The British were quick to appreciate the role of seaborne aircraft, and converted vessels such as *Ben-my-Chree* to the seaplane tender role.

Ben-my-Chree, a former passenger vessel on the Isle of Man route, was converted into a seaplane carrier in 1915. She was fitted with a large hangar aft, plus a flying-off ramp on the foredeck, and equipped with the new Sopwith Schneider seaplane fighters. This aircraft had a 100hp (73kW) rotary engine, an upward-firing Lewis gun and the ability to climb to 3048m (10,000ft) in a little over 30 minutes. With such improvements as these, the Sopwith Schneider presented the first serious threat to the Zeppelin airships which were attacking targets in Great Britain.

Direct hit

In May 1915 the *Ben-my-Chree* deployed to the Dardanelles, carrying two Short seaplanes equipped to launch torpedoes. On 12 August, Flight Commander C.H.K. Edmonds took off from the Gulf of Xeros and flew over the Bulair Peninsula into the straits, where he sighted an enemy transport. Descending to within 6m (20 ft) of the water, he launched his torpedo from 274m (300 yards) and scored a direct hit. Five days later, he torpedoed another transport. On the same day, the pilot of another Short had just landed on the water with a misfiring engine when he saw an enemy tug a few hundred yards away. He launched his torpedo while taxiing and saw the vessel blow up and sink. While anchored in Kastelorgio harbour in 1917, *Ben-my-Chree* was attacked by Turkish shore batteries and sunk.

Before her deployment to the Dardanelles *Ben-my-Chree* was used in an anti-Zeppelin role in the North Sea.

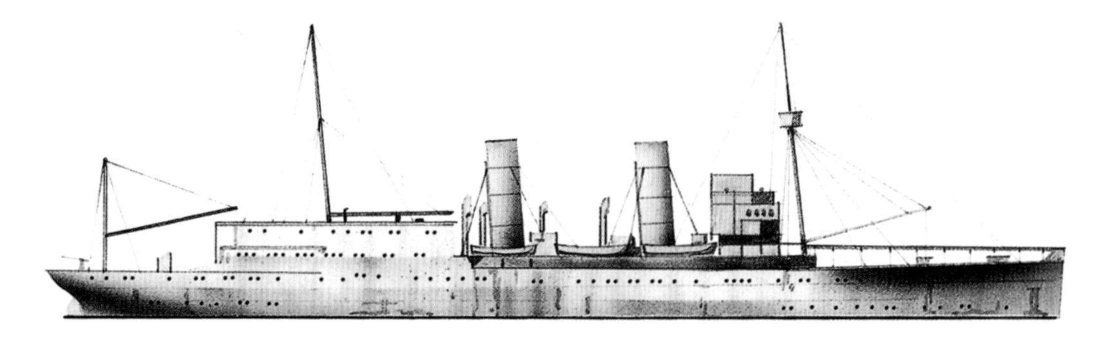

Danton

The *Danton* and her sister vessels were the first large French warships to be fitted with turbines, but they were already obsolescent when they were laid down

Twice torpedoed by the U64, *Danton* sank southwest of Sardinia in March 1917 with heavy loss of life.

COUNTRY:	France
TYPE:	Battleship
LAUNCH DATE:	4 July 1909
CREW:	753, later 923
DISPLACEMENT:	19,761 tonnes (19,450 tons)
DIMENSIONS:	146.5m x 25.8m x 9m (481ft x 84ft 8in x 28ft 8in)
RANGE:	6066km (3370nm) at 10 knots
ARMAMENT:	Four 304mm (12in) guns
POWERPLANT:	Quadruple screw turbines
PERFORMANCE:	19.3 knots

Danton and her five sisters were the last battleships to be built for the French Navy before the British all-big-gun battleship *Dreadnought* appeared on the scene and revolutionized naval development. *Danton*'s class contained powerful vessels, but it was too late to provide a serious challenge to the dreadnoughts then entering service.

Leader of the French revolution

Named after Georges Jacques Danton, a leader of the French Revolution, the battleship was laid down at Brest in 1908, launched in July 1909, and completed in 1911.

Danton saw initial war service in escorting Mediterranean convoys. On 19 March 1917, en route from Toulon to Corfu, she was hit by two torpedoes from the German submarine U64 and sank southwest of Sardinia with the loss of 296 lives. *Danton*'s sister pre-dreadnoughts were the *Condorcet*, *Diderot*, *Mirabeau*, *Vergniaud,* and *Voltaire*. *Condorcet* was damaged by explosions at Toulon in 1942 but not sunk, and was used as an accommodation ship by the Germans until she was severely bombed in 1944; she was scrapped in 1959. *Diderot* was broken up in 1936, *Mirabeau* and *Vergniaud* in 1928, and *Voltaire* in 1938.

***Danton* was not an aesthetically pleasing warship. The five funnels gave her a distinctive silhouette.**

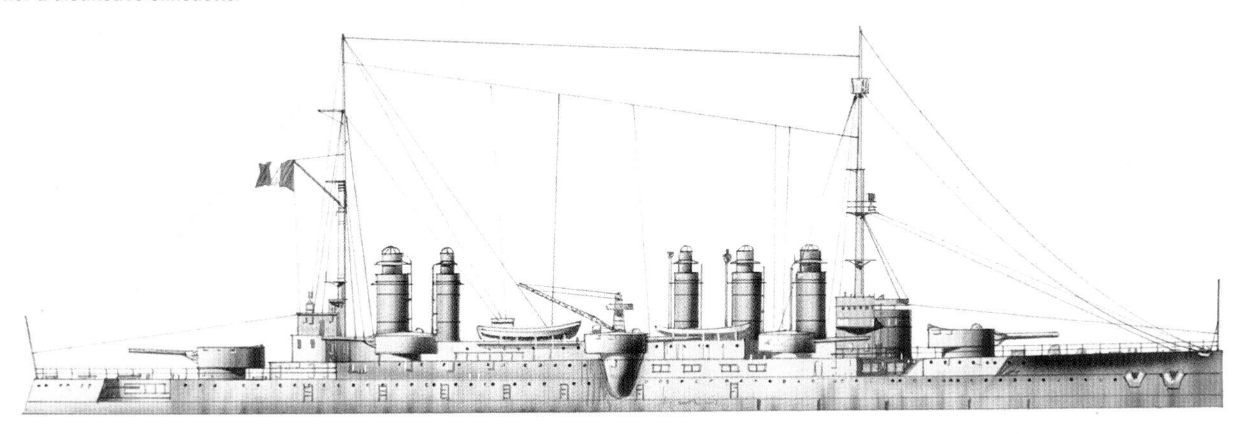

Conte di Cavour

After her reconstruction in the 1930s the *Conte di Cavour* emerged as a fine new battleship, but her contribution to the Italian Battle Fleet was to be short-lived.

COUNTRY: Italy
TYPE: Battleship
LAUNCH DATE: 10 August 1911
CREW: 1200
DISPLACEMENT: 29,496 tonnes (29,032 tons)
DIMENSIONS: 186m x 28m x 9m (611ft 6in x 91ft 10in x 30ft)
RANGE: 8640km (4800nm) at 10 knots
ARMAMENT: 10 320mm (12.6in), 12 120mm (4.7in) guns
POWERPLANT: Twin screw turbines
PERFORMANCE: 28.2 knots

The battleship *Conte di Cavour* was named after Count Camillo Benso di Cavour, statesman and architect of the unification of Italy.

Designed in 1908 and completed in 1914, *Conte di Cavour* saw war service in the southern Adriatic, and in 1919 she engaged in a cruise to the USA. In 1923 she operated in support of Italian troops occupying the island of Corfu. She was extensively rebuilt between 1933 and 1937 and emerged as a virtually new ship. She had new machinery and her hull was lengthened.

Attack by British Fairey Swordfish

On 11 November, 1940, she was at anchor in the naval base at Taranto when she and other warships were attacked by Fairey Swordfish aircraft from the British carrier HMS *Illustrious*. One, flown by Lt Cdr K. Williamson, passed over the stern of the battleship *Diga di Tarantola* and released its torpedo at the destroyer *Fulmine*. It missed, but exploded against the *Conte di Cavour*. The Italian battleship settled on the bottom. She was later refloated and towed to Trieste. She was rebuilt but, following the Italian surrender, was seized by the Germans in September 1943, and eventually sunk during an air raid in 1945. Her wreckage was broken up at the end of World War II.

The *Conte di Cavour*, shown here after reconstruction, was extensively rebuilt between 1933–1937, emerging as an almost new ship.

Gangut

The Russian parliament objected strenuously to the building of new dreadnoughts like *Gangut* on the grounds of the huge cost, but the plan was forced through and the battleships authorized by Tsar Nicholas II himself.

COUNTRY: Russia	
TYPE: Battleship	
LAUNCH DATE: 17 October 1911	
CREW: 1126	
DISPLACEMENT: 26,264 tonnes (25,850 tons)	
DIMENSIONS: 182.9m x 26.9m x 8.3m (600ft x 88ft 3in x 27ft 3in)	
RANGE: 7412km (4000nm) at 16 knots	
ARMAMENT: 12 305mm (12in), 16 120mm (4.7in) guns	
POWERPLANT: Quadruple screw turbines	
PERFORMANCE: 23 knots	

The heavy guns of *Gangut* – then renamed *Oktaybrskaya Revolutsia* in 1919 – played a major part in the defence of Leningrad during WWII.

Launched in 1911, *Gangut* and her three sisters were Russia's first dreadnoughts. The contract was won by Blohm and Voss, Hamburg, but the Russian government refused funds unless they were built in Russia. Russian industry could not produce enough high-tensile steel so an ingenious construction method was used, based upon the Italian *Dante Alighieri*, but building time was lengthy.

Reluctant to take the risk

Gangut was finally completed in 1914, but she was already largely obsolete, though her main guns were the largest then at sea. *Gangut* and her sister ships saw little action in World War I, not became their captains lacked offensive spirit, but because the Naval High Command had bitter memories of the 1905 defeat inflicted on the Russian fleet by the Japanese, and were reluctant to risk their vessels in the part of the Baltic where German submarines operated in strength. So operations were restricted to the Gulf of Finland. *Gangut* was deactivated in January 1918 and remained at Kronshtadt. In the 'Winter War' against Finland (1939–40) she was used to bombard Finnish shore positions. In September 1941, while taking part in the defence of Leningrad, she was severely damaged by six bombs during a Stuka attack, and was again hit by four bombs in April 1942. She was scrapped in 1956–9.

Gangut and her sister ships formed the First Battleship Brigade, operating from Helsinki. They seldom ventured out.

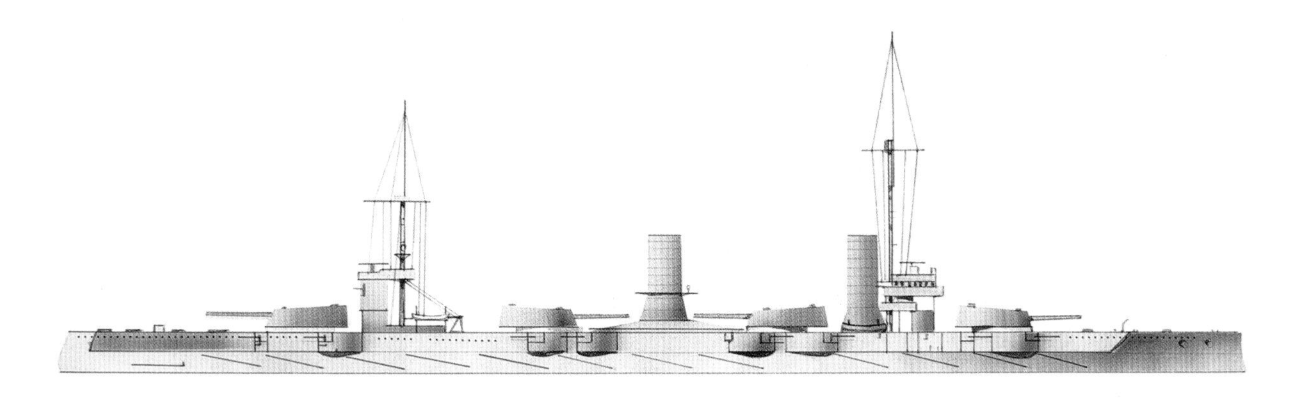

Giulio Cesare

When Italy entered World War I in 1915 her fleet included six dreadnoughts, one of which was the *Giulio Cesare*. In common with the rest of the Italian main fleet she achieved little during the conflict.

The *Giulio Cesare* ended her career in the service of the Soviet Navy, in which she served as the *Novorossisk*.

COUNTRY: Italy

TYPE: Battleship

LAUNCH DATE: 15 October 1911

CREW: 1235

DISPLACEMENT: 29,496 tonnes (29,032 tons)

DIMENSIONS: 186.4m x 28m x 9m (611ft 6in x 92ft x 30ft)

RANGE: 8640km (4800nm) at 10 knots

ARMAMENT: 12 120mm (4.7in), 10 320mm (12.6in) guns

POWERPLANT: Quadruple screw turbines

PERFORMANCE: 28.2 knots

Designed in 1908 by Engineer-General Masdea, *Giulio Cesare* and her two sisters were the first large group of Italian dreadnoughts. *Giulio Cesare* was completely rebuilt between 1933 and 1937, emerging with improved protection, new machinery and revised armament.

Serving in two world wars

She served in the Adriatic during World War I and saw early action against the British Mediterranean Fleet in World War II, being hit by the battleship *Warspite* in the Ionian Sea in July 1940. This occurred when a British naval force intercept the Italian fleet and cut it off from its main naval base at Taranto. HMS *Warspite* made contact with *Giulio Cesare* and opened fire on her from a range of 23,790m (26,000 yards), severely damaging her and slowing her to 18 knots. The Italian commander at once broke off the action and headed for the Italian coast accompanied by the *Cesare*'s sister ship *Conte di Cavour*. She was damaged by a near miss in an air raid on Naples in January 1941, and in December took part in the Battle of Sirte. In September 1943 she sailed for Malta to surrender to the Allies. At the end of World War II the ship was handed over to the Soviet Union and renamed *Novorossisk*. She served in the Black Sea until 1955.

Italy's new dreadnoughts were fine ships, and emerged from their post-war reconstruction fit to do battle with the Royal Navy.

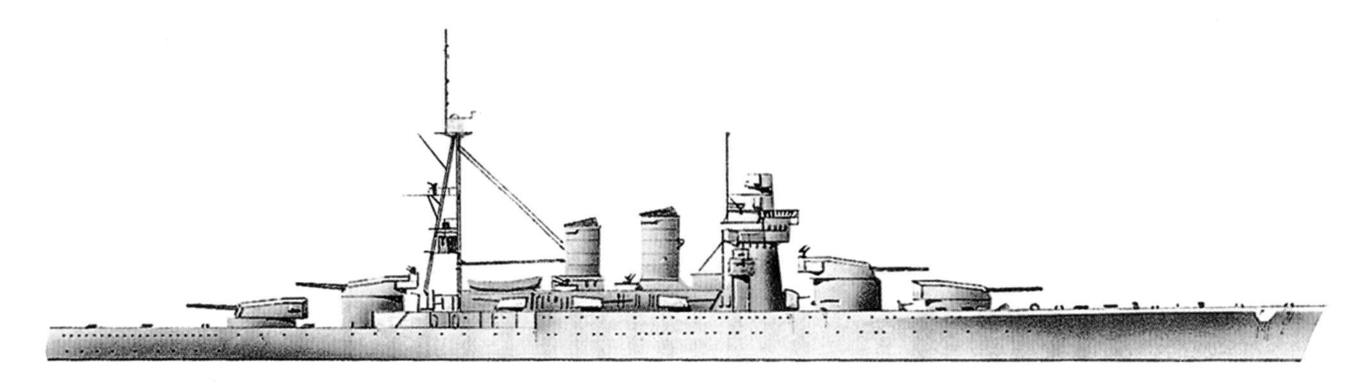

Goeben

The *Goeben* and her sister ship, *Moltke*, were improved versions of the earlier von der Tann class, with increased size and a modified hull form.

COUNTRY: Germany	
TYPE: Battleship	
LAUNCH DATE: 28 March 1911	
CREW: 1053	
DISPLACEMENT: 25,704 tonnes (25,300 tons)	
DIMENSIONS: 186.5m x 29.5m x 9m (611ft 10in x 96ft 9in x 29ft 6in)	
RANGE: 7634km (4120nm) at 14 knots	
ARMAMENT: 12 150mm (5.9in), 10 280mm (11in) guns	
POWERPLANT: Quadruple screw turbines	
PERFORMANCE: 28 knots	

The pursuit of the battlecruiser *Goeben* by British warships in the Mediterranean made headlines in 1914.

Goeben was one of two ships in the Moltke class that formed the second group of battlecruisers built for the German Imperial Navy before World War I. With the outbreak of war, *Goeben* and her consort *Breslau* were pursued across the Mediterranean by British ships *Indomitable* and *Indefatigable*, but they easily outran the British and put into the port of Constantinople. Both ships were transferred to the Turkish Navy. *Goeben* was renamed *Yavuz Sultan Selim* in 1914; in November she was damaged in action with Russian battleships off Samsoun, in December she struck two mines on the approaches to the Bosphorus. She was again damaged by Russian warships in May 1915. In January 1918 she sank the British monitors *Raglan* and *M28* at Mudros, and was again damaged by mines afterwards. She was broken up in 1954.

The end of the Magdeburg class

Goeben's companion, SMS *Breslau*, was one of four Magdeburg class light cruisers laid down in 1910. The class leader, *Magdeburg*, ran aground during a minelaying sortie in 1914 and was destroyed by Russian cruisers. The Russians captured her codebooks and passed them on to British Intelligence. The *Breslau* was incorporated into the Turkish Navy as the *Midilli*. She sank after striking five mines during a sortie against Imbros Island.

***Goeben* had a long career with the Turkish Navy, serving with distinction in the Black Sea. She was not laid up until 1948, and was broken up six years later.**

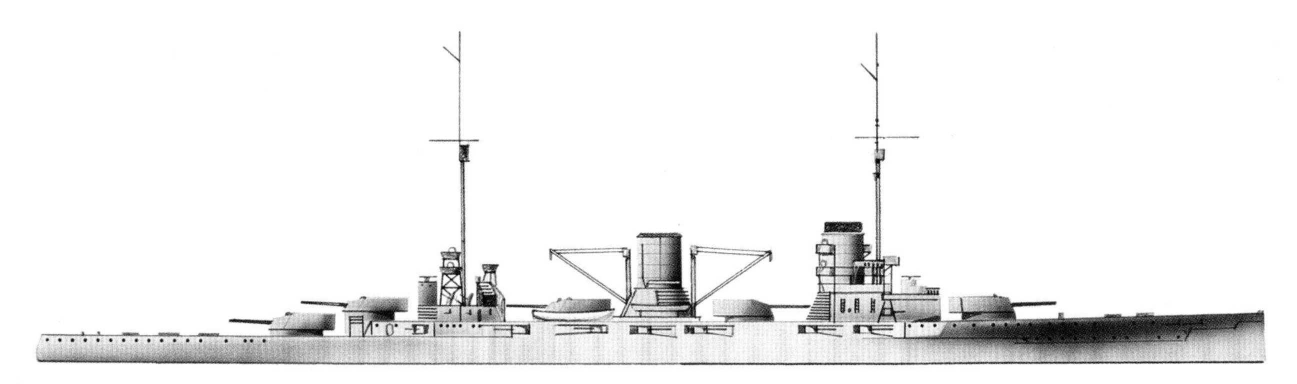

Iron Duke

During the Battle of Jutland, *Iron Duke* was the flagship of Admiral Jellicoe, commanding the Main Battle Fleet. It was her only action until 1939, when her guns were used against the German aircraft that ended her career.

COUNTRY: Great Britain
TYPE: Battleship
LAUNCH DATE: 12 October 1912
CREW: 1022
DISPLACEMENT: 30,866 tonnes (30,380 tons)
DIMENSIONS: 189.8m x 27.4m x 9m (622ft 9in x 90ft x 29ft 6in)
RANGE: 14,000km (7780nm) at 10 knots
ARMAMENT: 12 152mm (6in), 10 342mm (13.5in) guns
POWERPLANT: Quadruple screw turbines
PERFORMANCE: 21.6 knots

The venerable battleship *Iron Duke* survived World War I only to be damaged beyond repair by air attack in the next war.

Launched in 1912, *Iron Duke* was the British flagship at the Battle of Jutland in 1916, and was one of the longest-serving pre-World War I dreadnought battleships. She was a member of a class of four vessels that formed the third group of super-dreadnoughts, all armed with 343mm (13.5in) guns, and the first major capital ships to revert to 152mm (6in) guns for anti-torpedo boat defence. *Iron Duke*'s action in the Battle of Jutland did not begin until 6.31 in the evening of 31 May 1916, when she engaged the leading ship of the German König Squadron. Shortly afterwards, Admiral Jellico ordered the 2nd Battle Squadron to take station ahead of *Iron Duke*, and during the next half-hour the British warships held their targets under intermittent but effective fire before the German fleet broke off the action and turned away.

Training ship to depot ship

Minor changes were later made to *Iron Duke*'s secondary armament. She became a training ship in 1931, and was a depot ship at Scapa Flow between 1939–45. On 17 October 1939 she was attacked by four Junkers Ju88 dive-bombers of I/KG30 while at anchor in Scapa Flow and had to be beached after sustaining damage from near-misses. She was finally scrapped in 1946.

***Iron Duke* served the Royal Navy well, both as the flagship of the Main Battle Fleet and later as a training vessel.**

Bretagne

In 1940, Bretagne was a key element of the French Navy. After France's surrender, Prime Minister Winston Churchill ordered the Royal Navy to sink her, and other warships, to prevent their seizure by the Germans.

COUNTRY: France
TYPE: Battleship
LAUNCH DATE: 21 April 1913
CREW: 1133
DISPLACEMENT: 29,420 tonnes (28,956 tons)
DIMENSIONS: 166m x 27m x 10m (544ft 8in x 88ft 3in x 32ft 2in)
RANGE: 8460km (4700nm) at 10 knots
ARMAMENT: 10 340mm (13.4in) guns
POWERPLANT: Quadruple screw geared turbines
PERFORMANCE: 20 knots

***Bretagne* spent almost the whole of her career in the Mediterranean, but protected Atlantic convoys in the early months of World War II.**

France found herself falling behind in the dreadnought naval race, so *Bretagne* and her sisters *Provence* and *Lorraine* were based on the design of the preceding Courbet class to cut down construction time. *Bretagne* served in the Mediterranean from 1916–18, then underwent a series of extensive modernizations up to 1935.

A grim necessity

With the surrender of France in 1940, *Bretagne* and other French naval warships were called upon to join a British alliance, but the French admiral Gensoul refused. British warships, their gunfire directed by Swordfish spotter aircraft from the carrier *Ark Royal*, opened fire on the French vessels in their anchorage at Oran in Algeria. *Bretagne* was blown up and capsized with the loss of 1012 lives. This attack on the French fleet was one of the most tragic, melancholy operations ever undertaken by the Royal Navy, but was seen as a grim necessity. It emphasized Britain's determination to fight a merciless war, no matter what the cost. Another French squadron, comprising the battleship *Lorraine*, four cruisers and a number of smaller warships, was at Alexandria, where it had been operating under the command of the British Mediterranean Fleet before France collapsed. Here, a peaceful agreement was reached and the French warships were deactivated.

The destruction of the *Bretagne* caused enormous bitterness in France, and led to much anti-British sentiment among certain factions.

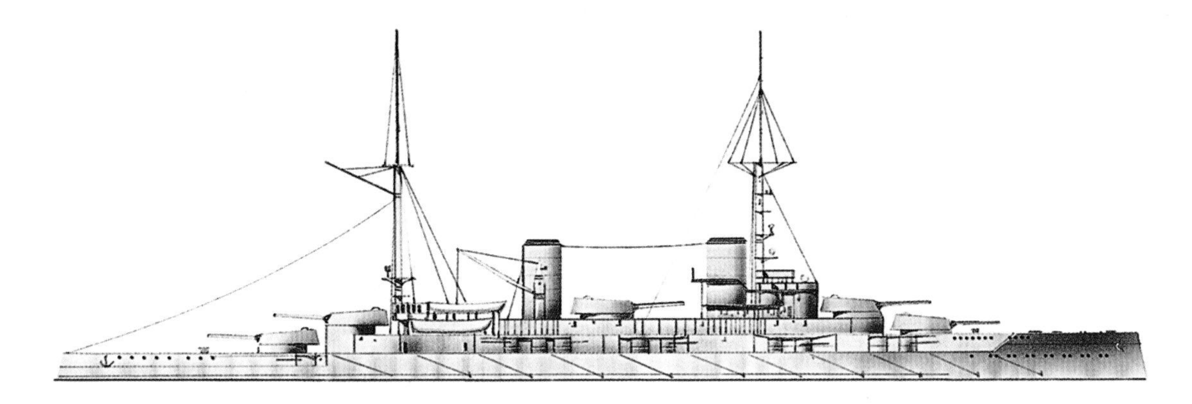

Andrea Doria

The battleship *Andrea Doria* had a very active career, surviving many naval actions in both world wars. She remained on active service until 1956.

COUNTRY: Italy
TYPE: Battleship
LAUNCH DATE: 30 March 1913
CREW: 1198
DISPLACEMENT: 26,115 tonnes (25,704 tons)
DIMENSIONS: 176m x 28m x 8.8m (577ft 5in x 91ft 10in x 28ft 10in)
RANGE: 8784km (4800nm) at 10 knots (before reconstruction)
ARMAMENT: 13 304mm (12in), 16 152mm (6in) guns
POWERPLANT: Twin shaft geared turbines
PERFORMANCE: 26 knots

The *Andrea Doria* underwent so much reconstruction between the two world wars that she emerged as virtually a new warship.

When Italy entered World War I in 1915 her fleet included six dreadnoughts, with four more under construction, one of which was the *Andrea Doria*. The Italian battle fleet achieved little during the war, its commanders failing to use their warships in an offensive fashion. Instead, they were preoccupied with defensive measures, moving the main operating base to Taranto, where it was safe from Austrian air attack.

Rebuilt and improved

Laid down in 1912, and completed four years later in 1916, *Andrea Doria*, and her sister ship *Caio Duilio*, both underwent a reconstruction programme from 1937 to 1940. *Andrea Doria*'s top speed was increased from 21.5 to 27 knots and she was given improved armour on her turrets and engine rooms. In World War I she operated in the southern Adriatic, and in 1919 in the Black Sea she supported the Allied Intervention Force operating in South Russia on the loyalist side during the civil war. In World War II *Andrea Doria* took part in convoy battles, including the First Battle of Sirte. She was placed on the Reserve in 1942, and in 1943 surrendered to the British at Malta. Both ships remained in service until 1958.

The *Andrea Doria* pictured before major reconstruction, following which she was recommissioned in 1940.

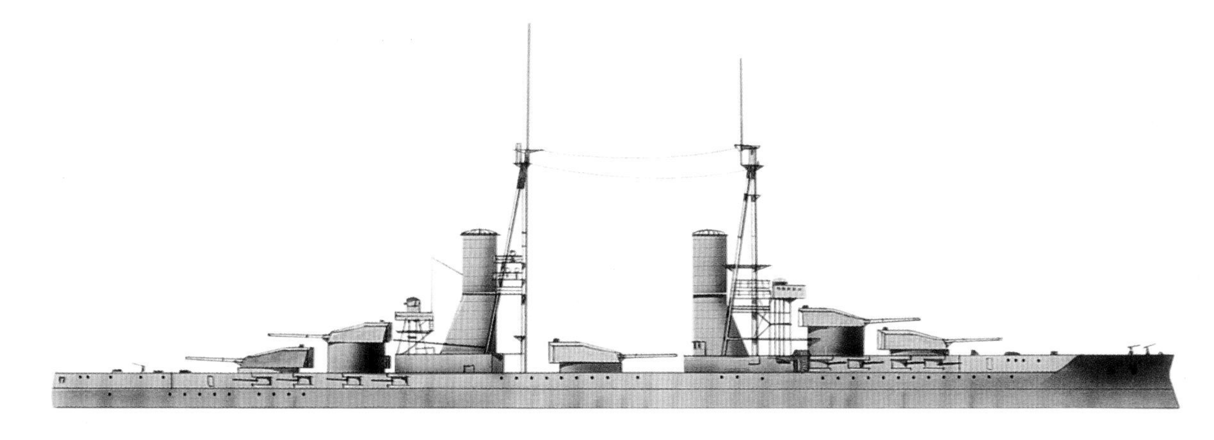

Canada

The construction of two modern warships for the Chilean Navy, of which the *Almirante Latorre* – later renamed *Canada* – was one, came about as the result of a border dispute with neighbouring Argentina.

COUNTRY: Chile
TYPE: Battleship
LAUNCH DATE: 27 November 1913
CREW: 1176
DISPLACEMENT: 32,634 tonnes (32,120 tons)
DIMENSIONS: 202m x 28m x 9m (660ft 9in x 92ft x 29ft)
RANGE: 8153km (4400nm) at 10 knots
ARMAMENT: 10 355mm (14in) guns
POWERPLANT: Quadruple screw geared turbines
PERFORMANCE: 22.8 knots

The *Canada* had a workmanlike design and saw war service with the Royal Navy during World War I before joining the Chilean Navy.

Ever since a Spanish naval squadron bombarded Valparaiso in 1866, the government of Chile made certain it had a powerful naval force at its disposal, and in 1879 the Chilean Navy, with the help of newly purchased ironclads, annihilated the navy of Peru, which had declared war. A border dispute with Argentina in the 1890s led to an arms race, Chile ordering the construction of two armoured cruisers and two battleships, the *Almirante Latorre* and the *Almirante Cochrane*. The battleships were laid down in British yards but had not been completed at the outbreak of World War I.

Taken over by the British

The most advanced of the two, the *Almirante Latorre*, was subsequently purchased by the Royal Navy and renamed *Canada*. Her sister ship, the *Almirante Cochrane*, was also taken over by the British and converted into a carrier named *Eagle*. *Canada* was a lengthened type of battleship like the *Iron Duke*. She had two large unequal funnels and a high tripod foremast and pole mainmast. Completed in 1915, *Canada* spent her entire war service with the Grand Fleet at Scapa Flow. One of the most effective battleships in the fleet, she saw action at the Battle of Jutland in 1916, and took part in the blockade of Germany. *Canada* was returned to Chile in 1920 and continued to see service as one of that country's capital ships.

Canada was launched on 27 November 1913 and completed in 1915, in time to take part in the Battle of Jutland in the following year.

Derfflinger

Given the inevitable nickname of 'Dirt Flinger' by her foes in the Royal Navy, the *Derfflinger* was without doubt one of the finest capital ships of her time.

A fine warship design, the *Derfflinger* gave rise to numerous improvements and was the first in a line of excellent vessels.

COUNTRY: Germany

TYPE: Battleship

LAUNCH DATE: 1 July 1913

CREW: 1112

DISPLACEMENT: 30,706 tonnes (30,223 tons)

DIMENSIONS: 210m x 29m x 8m (689ft x 95ft 2in x 27ft 3in)

RANGE: 10,080km (5600nm) at 12 knots

ARMAMENT: Eight 304mm (12in) guns

POWERPLANT: Quadruple screw turbines

PERFORMANCE: 28 knots

On 16 December 1914, *Derfflinger* was part of a force of German warships that bombarded Scarborough and Whitby, on the northeast coast of England; shortly afterwards, in January 1915, she was seriously damaged in the Battle of Dogger Bank. This action took place when the battlecruisers *Derfflinger*, *Seydlitz* and *Moltke*, and the armoured cruiser *Blücher*, set out on an offensive sweep of the southeastern Dogger Bank and encountered the British 1st Battlecruiser Squadron under Admiral Beatty.

Rugged survivor

The Germans turned and made for home, but were pursued and brought to battle east of the Dogger Bank. *Seydlitz* was also badly damaged and the *Blücher* sunk. In 1916, *Derfflinger* took part in the Battle of Jutland and blew up the British battlecruiser *Queen Mary* with 11 salvoes. However, she was hit by ten 380mm (15in) and ten 304mm (12in) shells. Despite fires on board, severe flooding and damage to her after-turrets she survived. *Derfflinger* and her two sister ships, *Hindenburg* and *Lutzow*, all of which had been launched in 1913, were arguably the best capital ships of their day. *Derfflinger* was scuttled at Scapa Flow in 1919 and raised for scrap in 1934.

The *Derfflinger* suffered battle damage that would have destroyed her equivalent battlecruisers in the Royal Navy.

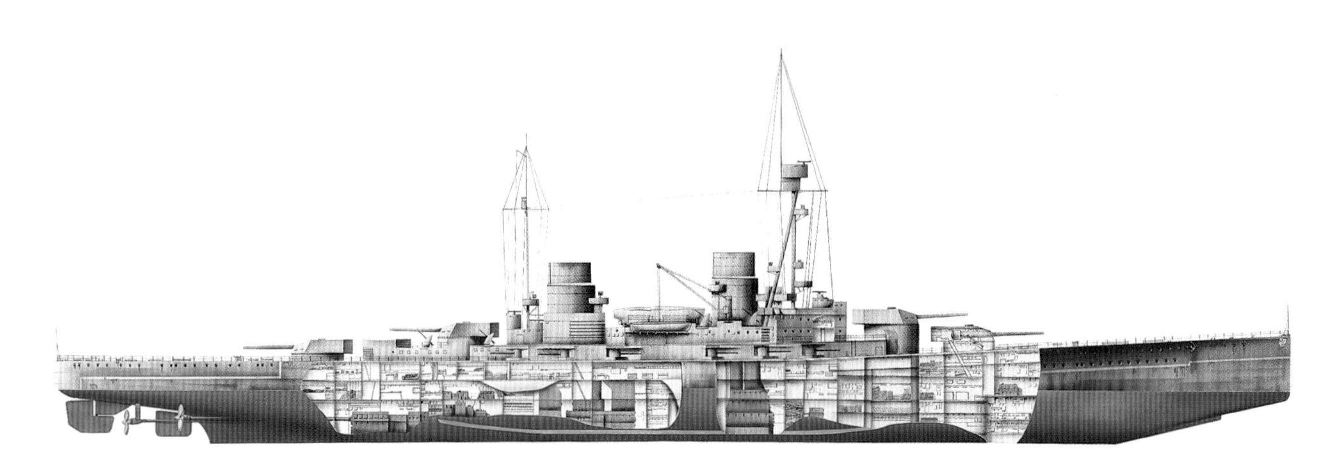

Caio Duilio

The *Caio Duilio* and her sister ship, *Andrea Doria*, were modified vessels of the Conte di Cavour class, fitted with secondary armament of 150mm (6in) guns. They underwent substantial reconstruction between the wars.

COUNTRY: Italy
TYPE: Battleship
LAUNCH DATE: 24 April 1913
CREW: 1198
DISPLACEMENT: 29,861 tonnes (29,391 tons)
DIMENSIONS: 187m x 28m x 8.5m (613ft 2in x 91ft 10in x 28ft 2in)
RANGE: 8640km (4800nm) at 12 knots
ARMAMENT: 10 320mm (12.6in) guns
POWERPLANT: Twin screw turbines
PERFORMANCE: 27 knots

The *Caio Duilio* spent most of her operational career in the Adriatic and the Black Sea during World War I.

Completed in 1916 as members of the Doria class, *Duilio* and her sister *Andrea Doria* underwent several changes in their careers, for example, receiving seaplanes in 1925. Extensive modernization between 1937 and 1940 upgraded both their armour and guns and turned both vessels into virtually new ships. *Duilio* was damaged in the British air attack on Taranto naval base, in November 1940. She was towed to Genoa for repair and narrowly escaped further damage when the port was bombarded by British warships in February 1941. Returned to active service later that year, she was employed on convoy interception and escort duty before being placed on the Reserve in 1942. After her surrender to the Allies at Malta in September 1943 she was used as a training ship. She was broken up at La Spezia in 1957. The British air attack on Taranto represented the first time that a formidable battle fleet had been crippled by carrier aircraft (a fact was not lost on the Japanese, who used it at Pearl Harbor).

Shattered morale

The effect on the morale of the Italian Navy was shattering. After Taranto, the Italian fleet was permanently on the defensive, the superiority of the Royal Navy in the Mediterranean assured. Italian warships would never again represent a serious threat to the security of the British convoys that were passing through the Mediterranean.

The *Caio Duilio* was named after Gaius Duilius, the general who was responsible for establishing Rome as a maritime power.

Grosser Kurfürst

The *Grosser Kurfürst* took her name from the distinguished military leader Friedrich Wilhelm, Elector of Brandenburg. She was the second vessel to bear the name, the first being a turret ship of 1872.

COUNTRY: Germany

TYPE: Battleship

LAUNCH DATE: 15 May 1913

CREW: 1136

DISPLACEMENT: 28,598 tonnes (28,148 tons)

DIMENSIONS: 175.7m x 29.5m x 8.3m (576ft 5in x 96ft 9in x 27ft 3in)

RANGE: 12,240km (6800nm) at 10 knots

ARMAMENT: Eight 86mm (3.4in) and 14 150mm (5.9in) guns

POWERPLANT: Triple screw turbines

PERFORMANCE: 21 knots

The *Grosser Kurfürst* and her sisters were the first German battleships to have all turrets on the centreline.

Turbines were used in German battleships for the first time on *Grosser Kurfürst* and her three sisters. The ships were greatly improved versions of *Helgoland*, and had superfiring guns aft, allowing the broadside to be increased from six to ten 305mm (12in) guns. Vessels of this class were contemporaries of the first British 343mm (13.5in) gunned battleships with similar displacement, but where the British had adopted the heavier guns and had only moderate protection, *Grosser Kurfürst* and her sisters retained the 305mm (12in) guns and used more armour.

Pushing a good strategy too far

Launched in 1913, *Grosser Kurfürst* saw action at the Battle of Jutland, taking eight hits. She surrendered at the end of World War I, and was scuttled with the rest of the German fleet in 1919. She was raised and scrapped in 1934. Her sister ships were *König*, *Kronprinz* and *Markgraf*; only *König* was not raised after scuttling. At the outbreak of war in 1913 the *Grosser Kurfürst* and all major German warships except the battlecruiser *Goeben* and von Spee's squadron in the Far East were in the North Sea area. These vessels collectively composed the German High Seas Fleet. Numerically inferior to the British Grand Fleet, they were capable of inflicting serious damage because of their better protection and standard of gunnery. The strategy of its commander, Admiral Scheder, was to force the British Fleet to divide its strength before engaging it. He tried to implement this strategy at Jutland, but ended up facing the entire Grand Fleet, with dire consequences.

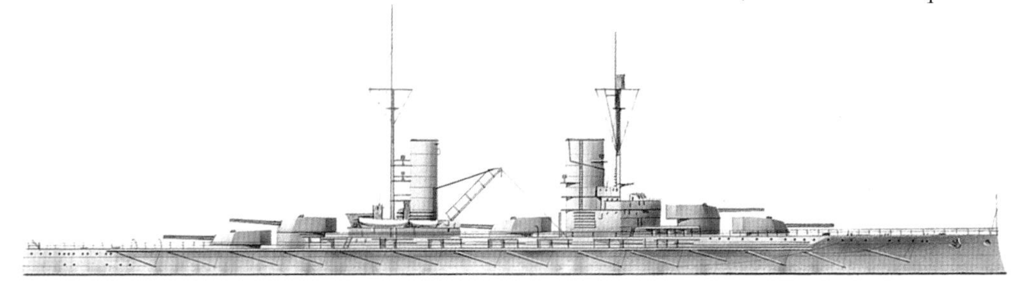

It was planned that all four ships of *Grosser Kurfürst*'s class would have diesel engines in place of one of their turbines.

Haruna

The *Haruna*, named after a mountain in north central Honshu, was laid down as a battlecruiser, but was reclassified as a battleship after reconstruction.

Like other Japanese battleships, the *Haruna* had a tall and crowded superstructure that made her appear top heavy.

COUNTRY: Japan	
TYPE: Battleship	
LAUNCH DATE: 14 December 1913	
CREW: 1221	
DISPLACEMENT: 32,715 tonnes (32,200 tons)	
DIMENSIONS: 214.5m x 28m x 8.4m (703ft 9in x 91ft 10in x 27ft 6in)	
RANGE: 14,400km (8000nm) at 12 knots	
ARMAMENT: 16 152mm (6in), eight 355mm (14in) guns	
POWERPLANT: Quadruple screw turbines	
PERFORMANCE: 27.5 knots	

Haruna was one of the first dreadnought-type warships to be laid down in a Japanese yard, and her sister *Kongo* was the last major Japanese warship to be built abroad. The four ships in *Haruna*'s class originally had three funnels and light military masts. In 1927–28 Haruna was refitted and reclassified as a battleship. The fore funnel was removed, and the second enlarged and heightened. Sixteen new boilers were installed, bulges were fitted and the armour thickened, increasing the total weight from 6606 tonnes (6502 tons) to 10,478 tonnes (10,313 tons). This increase was in direct contravention of the Washington Naval Treaty, which specified that no existing capital ship was to be rebuilt, although in recognition of developments in naval warfare, an increase in deck armour against air attack and the addition of anti-torpedo bulges were allowed, provided these modifications did not exceed a total of 3048 tonnes (3000 tons).

Attending every major action

In December 1941 she formed part of the distant-covering force for the Japanese landings in Malaya and the Philippines and then took part in every major action of the Pacific War. *Haruna* was sunk by US aircraft in July 1945. She was raised and broken up in 1946.

In common with other rebuilt Japanese capital ships, *Haruna* looked as though parts of her superstructure had been added haphazardly.

E-Class Submarines

The British E-class submarines of World War I were the best of their kind, operating with great success in the Mediterranean, North Sea and Baltic. Over one-third of the class was lost.

COUNTRY: Great Britain

TYPE: Attack submarine

LAUNCH DATE: 1913

CREW: 30

DISPLACEMENT: Surfaced: 677 tonnes (667 tons), submerged: 820 tonnes (807 tons)

DIMENSIONS: 55.17m x 6.91m x 3.81m (181ft x 22ft 8in x 12ft 6in)

SURFACE RANGE: 6035km (3579nm)

ARMAMENT: Five 457mm (18in) torpedo tubes; one 12-pounder gun

POWERPLANT: Two twin-shaft diesel engines, two electric motors

PERFORMANCE: Surfaced: 14 knots, submerged: 9 knots

This highly successful E11 is greeted with cheers as she returns from a war patrol in the Mediterranean.

The E class, a straightforward development of the D, was just beginning to enter service at the outbreak of World War I. The boats carried 30 crew and were armed with five torpedo tubes, two in the bow, one in the stern and two amidships. This meant the boat had to turn through no more than 45 degrees to engage any target. These became the mainstay of the Royal Navy's submarine fleet in World War I. Completed between 1913 and 1916, the E-class submarines ran to 55 hulls whose construction, once war was declared, was shared between 13 private yards. They fell into five major groups, differences being primarily in torpedo layout and the adaptation of six boats to carry 20 mines in place of their amidships tubes. E11, under the command of the talented Lt Cdr Martin Nasmith, was arguably the most famous; in the Dardanelles area she scored many successes, including the sinking of the Turkish battleship *Hairredin Barbarossa*. Many RN submariners who rose to high rank learned their trade in E-class boats.

Camouflage in shallow waters

For operations in the Dardanelles, the British submarines adopted a blue camouflage to conceal themselves in the shallow, clear waters. The class was also active in the North Sea and the Baltic. In all, 22 were lost.

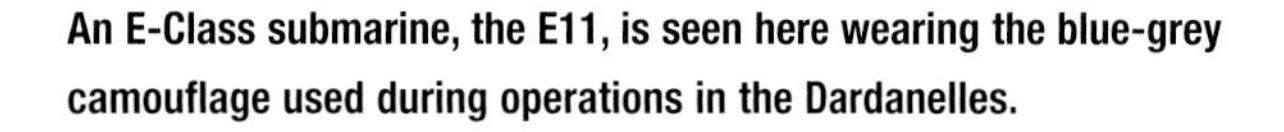

An E-Class submarine, the E11, is seen here wearing the blue-grey camouflage used during operations in the Dardanelles.

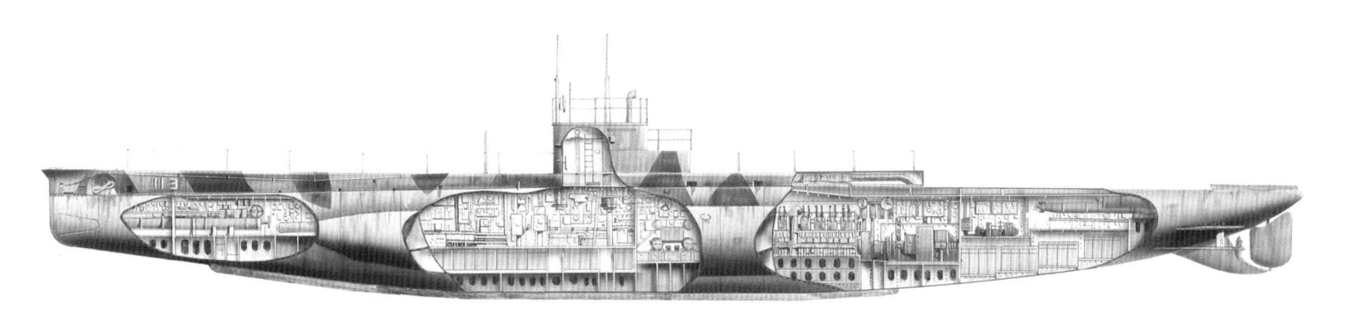

Barham

One of five ships of the Queen Elizabeth class, *Barham* was similar to the *Iron Duke* in layout. She was initially designed with five turrets, but one was deleted to make space for extra boilers.

COUNTRY: Great Britain
TYPE: Battleship
LAUNCH DATE: 31 October 1914
CREW: 951
DISPLACEMENT: 32,004 tonnes (31,500 tons)
DIMENSIONS: 196m x 27.6m x 8.8m (643ft x 90ft 6in x 29ft)
RANGE: 26,100km (14,500nm) at 10 knots
ARMAMENT: Eight 381mm (15in), 14 152mm (6in) guns
POWERPLANT: Four shaft turbines
PERFORMANCE: 24 knots

Because of the outbreak of war, *Barham* missed the modernization programme that would have given her heavier anti-torpedo armour.

By the time the Queen Elizabeth class ships were laid down in 1912-13, the British Admiralty had concluded that a battle fleet would be better protected by a wing of fast battleships on its flanks than by a force of battlecruisers scouting ahead. Much attention was paid to armament, which was the most modern available. *Barham* and her three sisters were designed to compete with new battleships (with 355mm [14in] guns) being designed by Germany, Japan and the USA. The class was equipped with newly designed 380mm (15in) guns, and also carried a much bigger bursting charge. *Barham* was badly damaged at Jutland in 1916, but all ships in the class underwent modernization in the early 1930s. *Barham* was sunk with heavy loss of life off Sollum in the Mediterranean by U331 on 25 November 1941. The other ships in *Barham*'s class were *Malaya*, *Queen Elizabeth*, *Valiant* and *Warspite*. After extensive war service, they were broken up in 1947–8. *Valiant* and *Queen Elizabeth* were badly damaged in a daring attack by Italian frogmen in Alexandria harbour in 1941.

Finished off by poor protection

Barham was to have been completely reconstructed, the work scheduled to begin in 1939, but this was cancelled following the outbreak of World War II. Better protection from torpedo attack might have saved her.

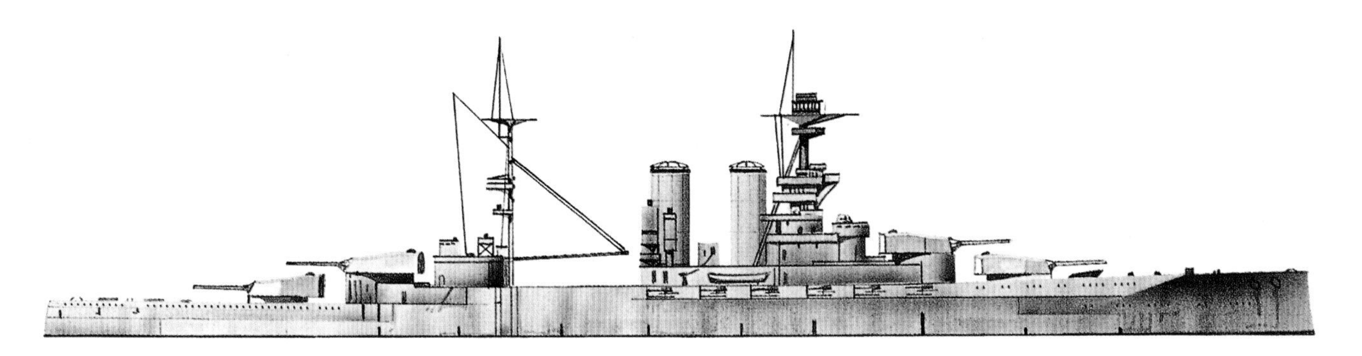

HMS *Barham* was easy to identify. Her main recognition feature was her twin funnels, set well forward and close together.

Fuso

Laid down just before the start of World War I as dreadnoughts, *Fuso* and *Yamashiro* were modernized in the 1920s, reclassed as battleships, and were brought up to a standard comparable with the ships of the US Fleet.

The *Fuso* is seen here after her reconstruction of 1933, when new engines and boilers were fitted and the forward funnel was removed.

COUNTRY:	Japan
TYPE:	Battleship
LAUNCH DATE:	28 March 1914
CREW:	1193
DISPLACEMENT:	36,474 tonnes (35,900 tons)
DIMENSIONS:	205m x 28.7m x 8.6m (672ft 6in x 94ft x 28ft)
RANGE:	14,400km (8000nm)
ARMAMENT:	12 356mm (14in), 16 152mm (6in) guns
POWERPLANT:	Quadruple screw turbines
PERFORMANCE:	23 knots

With the laying down of this vessel in March 1912 in a home yard, Japan confirmed her position as a leading naval power in the Pacific. Until then, all Japanese battleships had been built in British yards. *Fuso* and her sister *Yamashiro* were less heavily armoured than contemporary US battleships, but they had heavier armament and were two knots faster.

Too slow to venture far

Fuso had two funnels, with the first between the bridge and third turret. In the 1930s, this was replaced by a massive bridge structure. Underwater protection was improved and new machinery fitted. *Fuso* and *Yamashiro* both suffered from a slow maximum speed and spent most of the Pacific war in home waters, which resulted in their anti-aircraft armament remaining unchanged. It was planned to convert them into hybrid aircraft carriers after 1942, but the plan was abandoned after the Battle of the Marianas in 1944, when the Japanese Navy lost hundreds of aircrew. *Fuso* served in the Aleutians and at Leyte during World War II, and it was during the Battle of Leyte Gulf that she and the *Yamashiro* were sunk by gunfire and torpedoes from US battleships in October 1944.

At the time of their destruction at Leyte *Fuso* and *Yamashiro* had been fitted with a primitive form of radar.

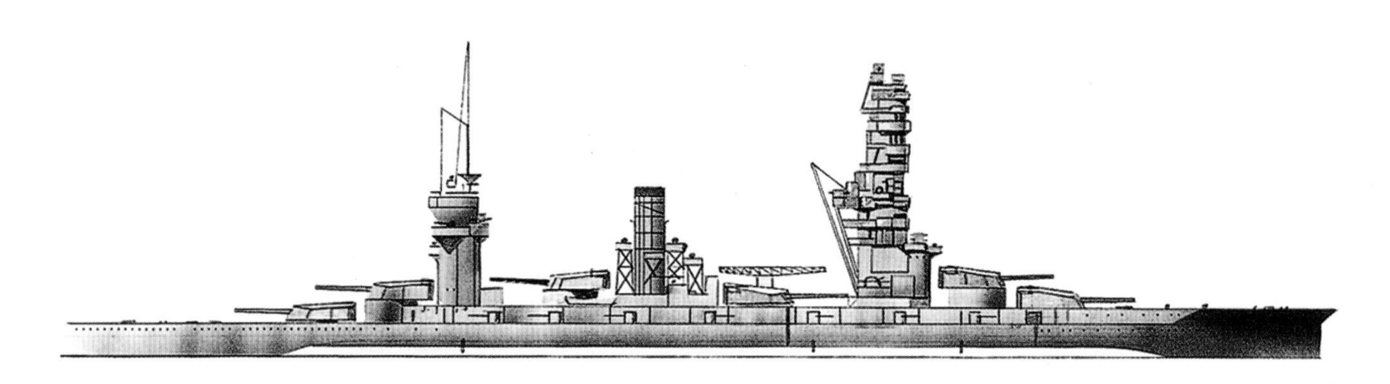

Baden

***Baden* was laid down at Schichau on 29 September 1913. It was first known as the *Ersatz Worth* (*Replacement Worth*), the latter being a pre-dreadnought in use as a coastal defence vessel and about to be retired.**

COUNTRY: Germany
TYPE: Battleship
LAUNCH DATE: 30 October 1915
CREW: 1271
DISPLACEMENT: 32,197 tonnes (31,690 tons) deep load
DIMENSIONS: 179.8m x 30m x 8.43m (589ft 10in x 98ft 5in x 27ft 8in)
RANGE: 9000km (5000nm) at 10 knots
ARMAMENT: Eight 380mm (15in), 16 150mm (5.9in) guns
POWERPLANT: Three shaft turbines
PERFORMANCE: 22 knots

The *Baden* was an important unit in Germany's High Seas Fleet, but was never used offensively.

Baden and her sister *Bayern* were completed in 1916. In contrast to earlier classes in the Imperial German Navy, their main armament was increased from 304mm (12in) to 380mm (15in). This was to match the guns rumoured to be carried on the new British Queen Elizabeth class.

A coal-fired ship

Unusually for a battleship of the period *Baden* was coal-fired, as wartime fuel oil supplies in Germany were too unpredictable. *Baden* was Fleet Flagship from October 1916, replacing Friedrich der Grosse, and surrendered in 1918, being substituted for the incomplete *Mackensen*. She was unsuccessfully scuttled at Scapa Flow in 1919, and after being salvaged by the Royal Navy was used as a gunnery target, then sunk. When the Allies demanded the surrender of further capital ships to compensate for those scuttled at Scapa Flow, the German Navy was reduced to a coastal defence force, armed with a motley collection of warships which included eight pre-war battleships, eight light cruisers, 32 destroyers and torpedo boats, some minesweepers and auxiliary craft. If new capital ships were built in the future to replace the old vessels, their displacement was not to exceed 10,000 tons.

***Baden* was a powerful warship with a heavy armament of eight 380mm (15in) guns, but arrived too late to have an impact on the war.**

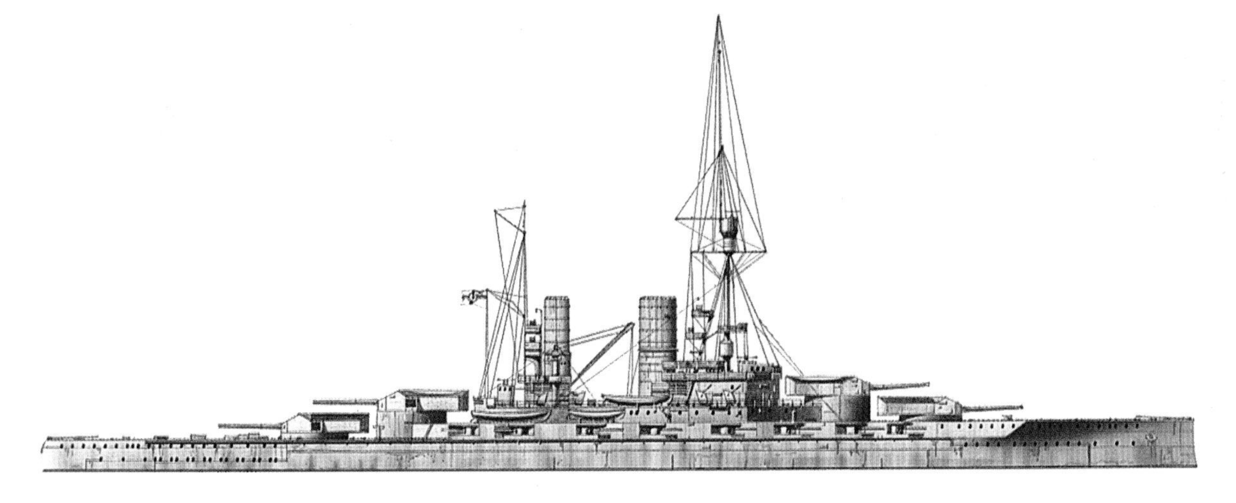

Arizona

The name of the battleship USS *Arizona* has become synonymous with the Japanese attack on Pearl Harbor. The great loss of life sustained among her crew strengthened American resolve to defeat Japan utterly.

COUNTRY: USA

TYPE: Battleship

LAUNCH DATE: 19 June 1915

CREW: 1117

DISPLACEMENT: 32,045 tonnes (32,567 tons)

DIMENSIONS: 185.4m x 29.6m x 8.8m (608ft x 97ft 1in x 28ft 10in)

RANGE: 14,400km (8000nm) at 10 knots

ARMAMENT: 12 356mm (14in), 22 127mm (5in) guns

POWERPLANT: Four shaft geared turbines

PERFORMANCE: 21 knots

The sinking of the *Arizona* by Japanese aircraft at Pearl Harbor, with heavy loss of life, caused outrage among the American public.

Arizona, like her sister ship *Pennsylvania*, was an improved and enlarged version of the Nevada class, her main armament being housed in four triple turrets. Launched in 1915, and completed the following year, *Arizona* did not see any action during World War I. In 1929-31 *Arizona* was completely reconstructed, her cagemasts being replaced by tripods, her secondary battery raised by one deck and aircraft catapults added on the stern and 'X' turret. She was also reboilered. Her sister ship, *Pennsylvania*, underwent further modernization in 1942, her tripod mainmast being replaced by a light pole mast and her armament improved. Both she and *Arizona* sailed to Pearl Harbor in 1941 to join the Pacific fleet. On the morning of 7 December the Japanese launched an air attack without warning. One of the first ships hit was *Arizona*. A bomb is believed to have struck one of her forward turrets, which detonated the magazine beneath. The ship blew up taking over a thousand of her crew with her.

Preserved as a war grave

Arizona was one of four US battleships to be sunk at Pearl Harbor; a fifth was beached and three more were damaged. Today her remains still lie in the shallow waters of the harbour where she is now preserved as a war grave.

The *Arizona* as she appeared after reconstruction in 1929-31. Her sister ship, *Pennsylvania*, was in dry dock when the Japanese struck.

Courageous

British aircraft carriers like *Courageous* were smaller than their US counterparts, but their greater numbers in the 1930s enabled the Royal Navy to deploy them among each of its fleets stationed throughout the world.

COUNTRY: Great Britain

TYPE: Aircraft carrier

LAUNCH DATE: 5 February 1916

CREW: 828

DISPLACEMENT: 26,517 tonnes (26,100 tons)

DIMENSIONS: 240m x 27m x 8m (786ft 5in x 90ft 6in x 27ft 3in)

RANGE: 5929km (3200nm) at 19 knots

ARMAMENT: 16 120mm (4.7in) guns, six flights of aircraft

POWERPLANT: Quadruple screw turbines

PERFORMANCE: 31.5 knots

HMS *Courageous* was an early casualty of World War II, being torpedoed two weeks after the start of hostilities.

Courageous and her sister *Glorious* were completed in 1917 as fast cruisers for service in the Baltic. Heavily armed with four 380mm (15in) guns, they had very little armour.

Converted to aircraft carriers

By the 1920s, Britain was anxious to increase her carrier strength, so both vessels, and their near sister *Furious*, were converted to aircraft carriers. The conversion of *Courageous* was completed in March 1928. Her superstructure and armament were replaced by an aircraft hangar running almost the length of the ship. The forward 18m (59ft) of the hangar was an open deck, which could be used to fly off slow-flying aircraft. Above this was an openflight deck, with two large elevators set into it. All three ships served through the 1930s, and formed the backbone of the British carrier force at the start of World War II. On 17 September 1939, the German submarine U-29, commanded by Lt Cdr Schuhardt, patrolling the Western Approaches, had been stalking what appeared to be a troopship when a dark smudge of smoke was sighted on the horizon to the west of the English Channel. It was *Courageous*, steaming towards the U-boat. Two hours later she was within range, her flank a perfect target. Schuhardt fired three torpedoes and then crash-dived to evade the carrier's escorting destroyers. The *Courageous* went down, taking her captain and over 500 of her crew with her.

In 1929 the carriers *Courageous*, *Furious* and *Eagle* operated in the Mediterranean, developing air strike tactics against warship targets.

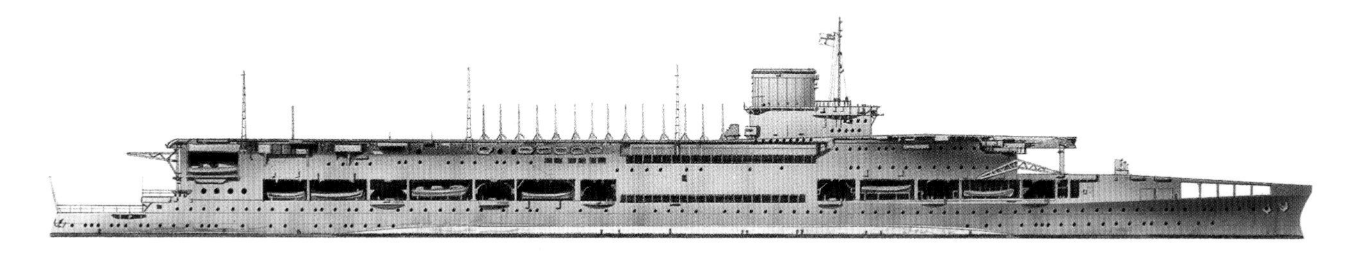

Furious

The origin of one of the best-known British aircraft carriers of World War II dates to pre-1914 when Jack Fisher, then First Sea Lord, planned for a fleet of fast, powerful cruisers with shallow draught to operate in the Baltic.

COUNTRY: Great Britain
TYPE: Aircraft carrier
LAUNCH DATE: 15 August 1916
CREW: 1218
DISPLACEMENT: 22,758 tonnes (22,400 tons)
DIMENSIONS: 239.6m x 27.4m x 7.3m (786ft 4in x 90ft x 24ft)
RANGE: 5929km (3200nm) at 19 knots
ARMAMENT: Six 102mm (4in) guns, 36 aircraft
POWERPLANT: Quadruple screw turbines
PERFORMANCE: 30 knots

HMS *Furious* was originally fitted with a safety net, seen here in the raised position, to stop aircraft running into the superstructure.

In 1917, the Royal Navy was at the forefront of the development of vessels fitted with flight decks from which landplanes could operate – the first true aircraft carriers. The first such ship was the light cruiser HMS *Furious*, laid down shortly after the outbreak of war. Launched on 15 August 1916, she was fitted initially with a flight deck forward of her superstructure, but was eventually completed with a continuous flight deck and hangar accommodation for 16 aircraft, which by early 1918 were all Sopwith camels. She was also fitted with workshops, electronically operated lifts from her hangar to the flight deck and a primitive form of arrester gear comprising strong rope nets suspended from cross pieces.

On 2 August 1917 Squadron Commander E.H. Dunning made the first ever landing by an aircraft on a ship under way, touching down in a Sopwith Pup on HMS *Furious*. He was killed on a second attempt.

An invaluable asset

After undergoing a more complete rebuild, she served with the Home and Mediterranean fleets in World War II. Together with HMS *Eagle*, she was an invaluable asset in the early months of the Mediterranean war, flying off fighter aircraft to Malta. Her aircraft attacked Tirpitz in 1944 and she was taken out of operational service the same year. She was scrapped in 1948.

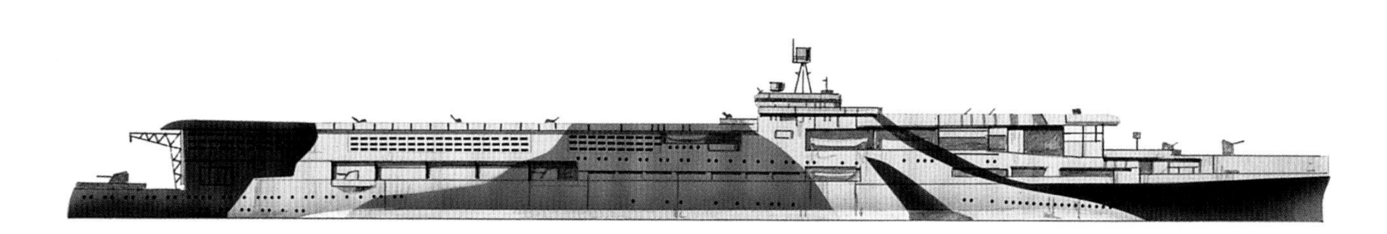

Idaho

The ships of the New Mexico class had hulls that were similar to the Pennsylvania class, with a 'clipper bow' and improvements to watertight compartments. All were reconstructed in the early 1930s.

COUNTRY: USA	
TYPE: Battleship	
LAUNCH DATE: 30 June 1917	
CREW: 1084	
DISPLACEMENT: 33,528 tonnes (33,000 tons)	
DIMENSIONS: 190.2m x 29.7m x 9.1m (624ft x 97ft 6in x 29ft 10in)	
RANGE: 14,400km (8000nm) at 10 knots	
ARMAMENT: 12 356mm (14in), 14 127mm (5in) guns	
POWERPLANT: Quadruple screw turbines	
PERFORMANCE: 21 knots	

This aerial view of the New Mexico class battleship USS *Idaho* was taken in New York harbour in May 1927.

Idaho was one of a trio of battleships of the New Mexico class that had a new 356mm (14in) gun that could be elevated independently; previously, all weapons in a turret had been locked into the same elevation. The main guns were housed in triple turrets. Originally 22 127mm (5in) guns were planned. The number was reduced to 14, allowing extra armour in some areas. *Idaho* was extensively rebuilt in 1930–31. From 1919 to 1941 she served with the Pacific fleet, being transferred to the Atlantic fleet for a brief period before returning to the Pacific. She subsequently fought actions off Attu, the Gilbert Islands, Kwajalein, Saipan, Guam, Palau, Iwo Jima and Okinawa, running aground off Okinawaw in June 1945. By 1943 she had had all her 127mm (5in) guns removed.

Bombarding Japanese-held islands

As the Pacific war progressed and the Imperial Japanese Navy became a rapidly diminishing threat, the role of the battleship increasingly switched from the protection of the carrier task forces to the heavy bombardment of Japanese-occupied islands prior to invasion by US forces. The last combat between battleships took place at Leyte in 1944, in the Battle of the Surigao Strait. *Idaho* was stricken in 1947; her sister ships were *New Mexico* and *Mississippi*.

This is how *Idaho* appeared after completion, fitted with cagemasts, which were later replaced during reconstruction.

Hood

HMS *Hood* had become synonymous with Britain's pride, thanks to her pre-war overseas cruises, so when she was sunk by the German battleship *Bismarck* in May 1941, the news came as a cruel blow to the British public.

COUNTRY: Great Britain
TYPE: Battlecruiser
LAUNCH DATE: 22 August 1918
CREW: 1477
DISPLACEMENT: 45,923 tonnes (45,200 tons)
DIMENSIONS: 262m x 31.7m x 8.7m (860ft x 104ft x 28ft 6in)
RANGE: 7200km (4000nm) at 10 knots
ARMAMENT: 12 140mm (5.5 in), eight 381mm (15in) guns
POWERPLANT: Quadruple screw turbines
PERFORMANCE: 32 knots

HMS *Hood*, suitably bedecked with bunting, pictured at the Coronation Review of the Fleet at Spithead in 1937.

Hood was to have been the first of four such ships, but was the only one completed. Her engines developed 144,000hp, and range was 7600km (4000 miles) at 10 knots. Despite these advantages, whilst engaging the German battleship *Bismarck* and the cruiser *Prinz Eugen* on 21 May 1941, her upper armour was breached by a shell, blowing her in two. Only three survived; 1338 were lost. The sinking of *Hood* was keenly felt by the British. She had 'shown the flag' for Britain several times, most notably in 1923, when she embarked on a world cruise. Her assailant, *Bismarck*, survived her by just three days before she too was sunk. HMS *Hood* was designed as an enlarged Queen Elizabeth class as a response to the formidable German Mackensen class battlecruisers then under construction. (They were never completed, but their design formed the basis of the later and even more formidable *Scharnhorst* and *Gneisenau*.)

A redesign that failed

Hood's original design was modified after the Battle of Jutland in 1916, when existing British battlecruisers took severe punishment. The redesign included greater armour protection; nevertheless, she remained poorly protected, and it was to be her downfall.

HMS *Hood*'s silhouette was famous around the world, and she was the pride of the Royal Navy.

Kaga

Launched on 17 November 1921, *Kaga* was originally laid down as an improved *Nagato*-type dreadnought, with increased armour protection and an enlarged main battery.

The *Kaga* was not a very satisfactory conversion, and was reconstructed in 1934–5, the flight deck being lengthened.

COUNTRY: Japan	
TYPE: Aircraft Carrier	
LAUNCH DATE: November 1921	
CREW: 2400	
DISPLACEMENT: 33,693 tonnes (33,160 tons)	
DIMENSIONS: 260.7m x 31.3 x 8.7m (855ft 3in x 102ft 7in x 28ft 5in)	
RANGE: 13,000km (7000nm)	
MAIN ARMAMENT: Ten 200mm (8in) guns; 16 120mm (4.7in) guns; 22 anti-aircraft guns	
POWERPLANT: Kanpon geared turbines	
PERFORMANCE: 31 knots	

In February 1922, *Kaga* was cancelled to comply with the terms of the Washington Naval Treaty, but instead of scrapping her the Japanese Naval Staff completed her as an aircraft carrier to replace another carrier, the *Amagi*, which had been destroyed in an earthquake while under construction. (A sister ship, *Tosa*, was stricken and her incomplete hull sunk as a target in 1925.)

Short but spectacular career

Kaga was completed in 1928 and joined the Combined Fleet in 1930. Reconstructed in 1934-5, she was fitted with a full-length flight deck and island. Recommissioned in June 1935, she was assigned to the 1st Carrier Division with the *Akagi*, her air group seeing action during the Sino-Japanese war. Her career during World War II was short but spectacular. In December 1941 her aircraft attacked Pearl Harbor and later operated over Rabaul, Darwin and Java. She then formed part of the Japanese carrier task force for the assault on Midway Island in June 1942. Concentrating on the destruction of Midway's air defences, the Japanese carriers were caught unprepared when American dive-bombers and torpedo-bombers launched their counterattack. *Akagi*, *Kaga* and *Soryu* were all sunk, *Kaga* sustaining 800 fatalities, many of them experienced aircrew. The Japanese Navy never recovered.

The carrier *Kaga* was named after a province of north central Honshu, largest of the Japanese home islands.

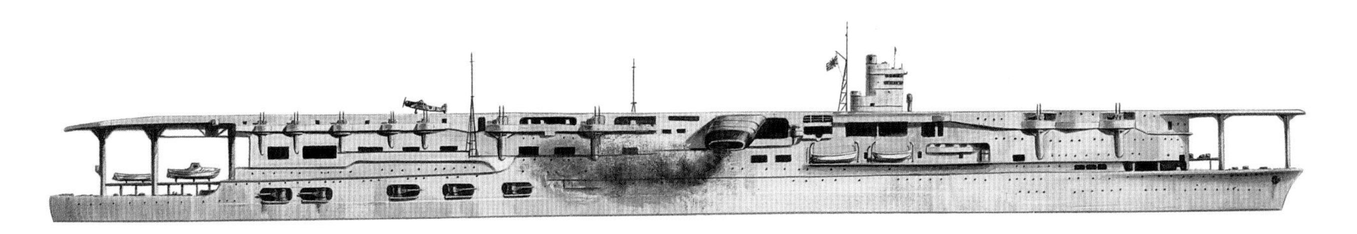

Kamikaze

All the vessels in this Japanese class of destroyer were originally assigned only numbers, names being allocated only in 1928. All were named after winds.

COUNTRY: Japan
TYPE: Destroyer
LAUNCH DATE: 25 September 1922
CREW: 148
DISPLACEMENT: 1676 tonnes (1650 tons)
DIMENSIONS: 102.6m x 9m x 2.89m (336ft 3in x 29ft 6in x 9ft 6in)
RANGE: 6670km (3601nm)
MAIN ARMAMENT: Four 120mm (4.7in) guns; six 533mm (21in) torpedo tubes
POWERPLANT: Two shafts, geared steam turbines
PERFORMANCE: 37.5 knots

Japan's destroyers, like the *Kamikaze*, were very effective warships, and in the 1920s were better than their Western counterparts.

Japan showed a great deal of initiative and originality in her destroyer design, some of those built in the 1920s being at the forefront of the world's navies in design and armament. For the first time, destroyers carried their main armament in enclosed turrets, which in later units elevated up to 75 degrees, making them useful anti-aircraft weapons. A 24-inch torpedo was also introduced in the Japanese destroyers, its existence kept a closely guarded secret. The name *Kamikaze* means 'Divine Wind'. Ordered between 1921 and 1922, the nine Kamikaze-class destroyers actually formed Group II of the preceding Minekaze class. They were the first destroyers in the Imperial Japanese Navy to be built with a bridge strengthened by steel plating. This gave them a high centre of gravity, which was counterbalanced by an increased displacement and slightly wider beam.

Surrender at Singapore

The ships of this class had a distinguished record in World War II. In 1944 four were sunk by US submarines and a fifth in an air attack on Truk. *Kamikaze* survived the war and was surrendered at Singapore, but in June 1946 she became stranded on a reef and was scrapped where she lay.

If the destroyers of *Kamikaze*'s class had a weakness, it was that their hulls lacked strength, making them susceptible to storm damage.

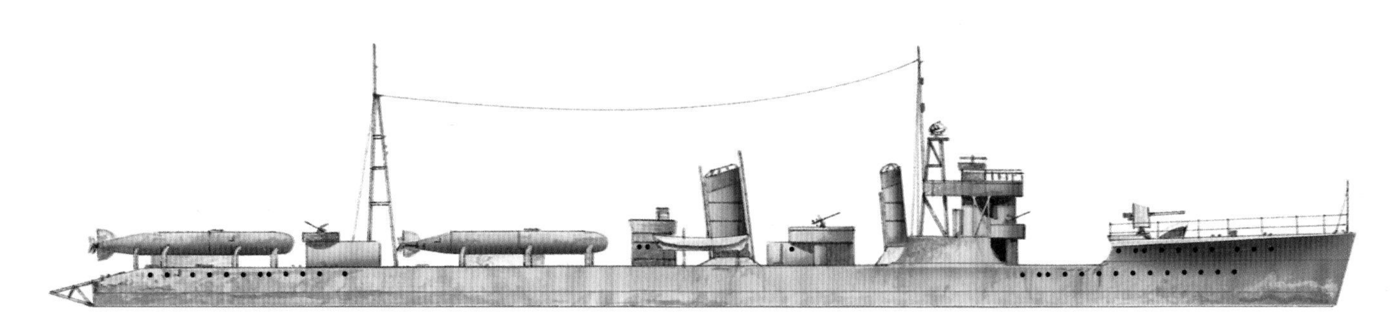

Lexington

The USS *Lexington* originated as a battlecruiser and was first classed as a battle scout – a ship powerful enough to carry out reconnaissance tasks in the face of enemy battlecruisers. Then she became an aircraft carrier.

COUNTRY: USA
TYPE: Aircraft carrier
LAUNCH DATE: 3 October 1925
CREW: 2327
DISPLACEMENT: 48,463 tonnes (47,700 tons)
DIMENSIONS: 270.6m x 32.2m x 9.9m (88ft x 105ft 8in x 32ft 6in)
RANGE: 18,900km (10,500nm) at 10 knots
ARMAMENT: Eight 203mm (8in), 12 127mm (5in) guns, 80 aircraft
POWERPLANT: Quadruple screw turbo electric drive
PERFORMANCE: 33.2 knots

Easily recognizable by her very prominent island, the *Lexington* was a fast ship, retaining her original battlecruiser hull form and machinery.

Lexington was the first fleet aircraft carrier completed for the US Navy. She was laid down in 1921 as a battlecruiser, but work was stopped as a result of the 1922 Washington Naval Treaty. Her design was changed to that of an aircraft carrier. A 137m x 21m (450ft x 70ft) hangar was installed and for many years she remained the largest aircraft carrier afloat. In May 1942 she was operating as part of Task Force 11, one of three Allied naval task forces which combined to thwart a Japanese landing at Port Moresby, New Guinea, in the Battle of the Coral Sea. In this, the first naval engagement in history fought without opposing ships making contact, the US carrier forces succeeded in turning back the covering Japanese carrier force, and aircraft from the carrier USS *Yorktown* attacked Japanese transports. On 7 May carrier aircraft located and sank the Japanese light carrier *Shoho*.

US naval observers learned from the fate of British battlecruisers at Jutland and decided *Lexington* needed better magazine protection.

Abandoned to her fate

The next day the Japanese covering force was attacked. Almost simultaneously, enemy torpedo aircraft attacked the US Task Force 17, damaging the *Yorktown* and starting uncontrollable fires on the *Lexington*, as a result of which she had to be abandoned. She was later sunk by the destroyer USS *Phelps*.

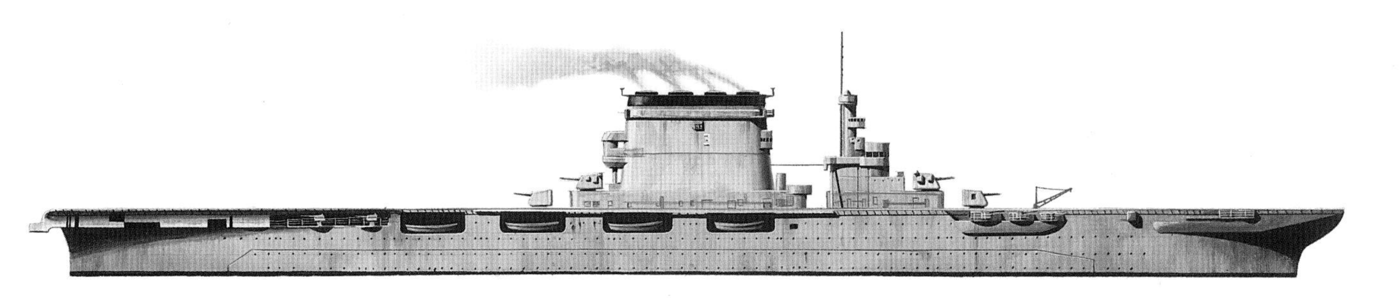

Nelson

HMS *Nelson* and her sister vessel, *Rodney*, were the first British battleships to be constructed after the end of World War I, being laid down under the terms of the Washington Naval Treaty.

COUNTRY: GREAT BRITAIN
TYPE: BATTLESHIP
LAUNCH DATE: 3 September 1925
CREW: 1361 (as flagship)
DISPLACEMENT: 38,608 tonnes (38,000 tons)
DIMENSIONS: 216.8m x 32.4m x 9.6m (711ft x 106ft 4in x 31ft 6in)
RANGE: 30,574 (16,500nm at 12 knots)
ARMAMENT: Nine 406mm (16in), 12 152mm (6in) guns
POWERPLANT: Twin screw turbines
PERFORMANCE: 23.5 knots

One of HMS *Nelson*'s claims to fame was that in September 1943 the armistice between Italy and the Allies was signed aboard her.

The main aim of the 1922 Washington Treaty, engineered by the USA and, in effect, the first arms limitation treaty in history, was to limit the size of the navies of Great Britain, the USA, France, Italy and Japan, the five principal maritime powers. For Britain, this meant a reduction in capital ship assets to 20 by scrapping existing warships and dropping new projects. But because her capital ships were older and less heavily armed than those of the USA, she would be allowed to build two new vessels as replacements. The new battleships were the *Nelson* and *Rodney*, both of which were laid down in December 1922.

Flagship of the Home Fleet

Nelson was completed in June 1927. Her layout was unusual, all her main guns being mounted forward. From 1927 to 1941 she was flagship of the Home Fleet, based at Scapa Flow in the Orkneys. She was damaged by a mine off Loch Ewe on 4 September 1939. On 27 September 1941 she was torpedoed by an Italian aircraft while on convoy escort duty in the Mediterranean, putting her out of action until August 1942. On 29 September 1943 the armistice agreement was signed on board her. On 12 July 1944, while part of the warship force off Normandy, she was torpedoed yet again, this time by the German motor torpedo boat S138. After repair at Philadelphia she deployed to the Eastern Fleet, ending her war in the Indian Ocean. She was broken up in 1948.

Nelson's design, with her main armament mounted well forward, gave her silhouette a curious unbalanced appearance.

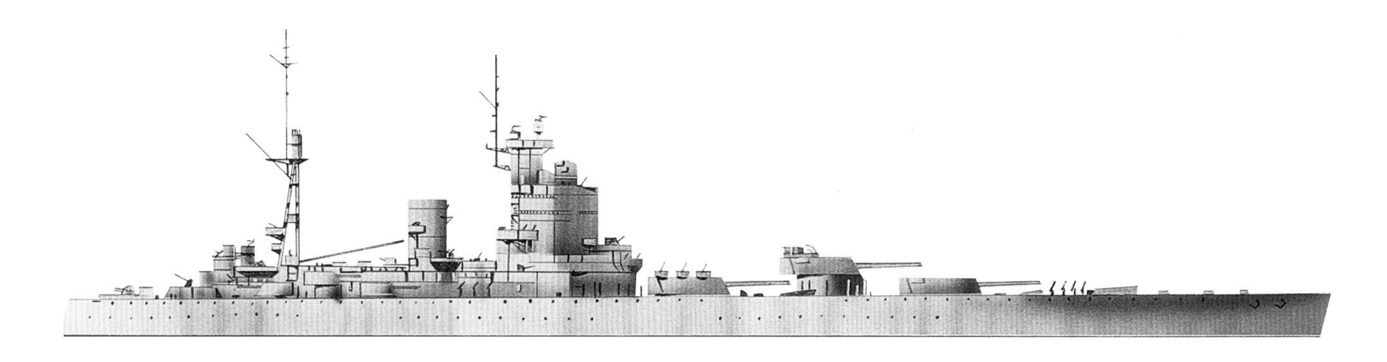

Fubuki

The *Fubuki* was one of the few Japanese warships to survive the war in a floating condition. Badly damaged in 1944, she was towed to Yokosuka for repairs and never re-emerged.

COUNTRY: Japan	
TYPE: Destroyer	
LAUNCH DATE: 15 November 1927	
CREW: 197	
DISPLACEMENT: 2123 tonnes (2090 tons)	
DIMENSIONS: 118.35m x 10.36m x 3.2m (388ft 3in x 34ft x 10ft 6in)	
RANGE: 8684km (4689nm)	
MAIN ARMAMENT: Three twin 127mm (5in) guns; three triple 610mm (24in) torpedo tubes	
POWERPLANT: Two sets of geared steam turbines	
PERFORMANCE: 37 knots	

The *Fubuki* and her sisters were among the world's finest destroyers and remained effective throughout World War II.

At the time of their construction between 1927 and 1931, the Fubuki-class ships were among the trend-setters of the destroyer world. Previously, Japanese destroyers had been influenced by British and German designs but now, Japanese designers went their own way to produce a destroyer so advanced it was still formidable at the end of World War II. Known to the Japanese Admiralty as 'Special Type' destroyers, they were among the finest afloat, their enclosed guns having an elevation of 40 degrees and consequently having a dual anti-aircraft role. In 1943, the X turret was removed from surviving Fubuki-class destroyers in favour of more light AA guns. The class served widely in all theatres of war. Only the *Ushio* survived the conflict. Badly damaged in Manila Bay on 14 November 1944, she was towed to *Yokosuka*, and surrendered there at the war's end.

Sunk by US warships

Fubuki herself was sunk by US warships off Guadalcanal on 11 October 1942. Of the other ships in the Fubuki class, one was sunk in a pre-war collision with a Japanese destroyer and 18 were war losses, two being mined, three being sunk in action with US surface forces, six being sunk by submarine torpedoes and the rest by air attack.

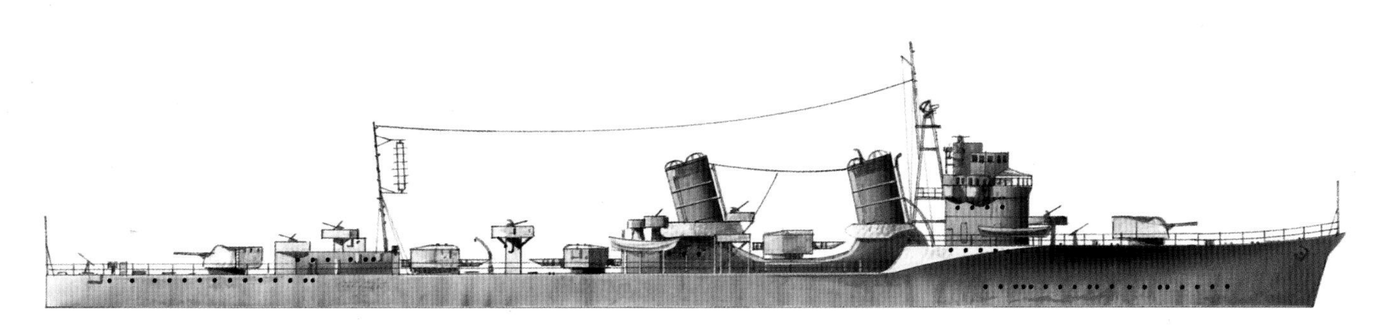

The rakish lines of the Fubuki class are apparent in this illustration. The destroyer's entire silhouette exudes speed.

Köln

Completed in 1928, the light cruiser *Köln* was in action from the very first day of World War II almost to the very end.

COUNTRY: Germany	
TYPE: Light cruiser	
LAUNCH DATE: 1928	
CREW: 850	
DISPLACEMENT: 7330 tonnes (6650 tons) standard; 8960 tonnes (8130 tons) full load	
DIMENSIONS: 570ft 10in x 50ft 2in x 18ft 3in (174m x 15.3m x 5.56m)	
RANGE: 4500nm (8338km) at 14 knots	
ARMAMENT: nine 5.9in (150mm); 12 19.7in TT	
POWERPLANT: two screws, geared turbines; 65,000hp	
PERFORMANCE: 32 knots	

Light cruisers were at the core of Germany's early naval expansion plans. First, in 1925, came the *Emden*, followed in 1927 by the *Karlsruhe*, the *Köln* (1928) and the *Leipzig* (1929). *Nürnberg* was launched in 1934, and the *Königsberg* in 1937. In the early weeks of World War II the *Köln* and *Leipzig* carried out mining operations in the North Sea, prior to participating in the invasion of Norway. After service in northern waters *Köln* deployed to the Baltic in 1941, where she formed part of a powerful naval battle group comprising the battleship *Tirpitz*, the heavy cruiser *Admiral Scheer*, the cruiser *Nürnberg*, three destroyers and five torpedo boats, engaged in blockading the Soviet Baltic Fleet in its naval base at Kronstadt.

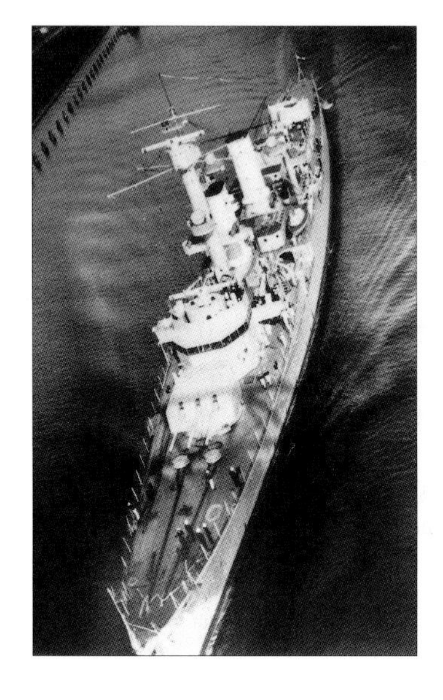

The light cruiser *Köln* gave excellent wartime service.

Heavy Damage

After further service in Norwegian waters she returned to the Baltic as part of the Fleet Training Squadron, where she operated alongside the other light cruisers. On 15 October 1944, *Leipzig* was badly damaged in collision with the heavy cruiser *Prinz Eugen* off Gdynia. *Köln* was bombed and sunk in an air attack while undergoing a refit at Wilhelmshaven on 30 April 1945, while *Leipzig* - having taken part in the evacuation of troops and civilians from East Prussia, despite her unseaworthy condition – surrendered to the Allies and was sunk in the North Sea in July 1946, laden with canisters of poison gas.

The *Köln* began life at the Wilhelmshaven naval dockyard, and ended it there when she was bombed and sunk by the RAF during a refit.

Ardent

HMS *Ardent* was one of the best destroyers to serve with any of the world's navies before and during World War II, in the course of which she met a gallant end.

HMS *Ardent* pictured at the Coronation Review of the Fleet in 1937. Many ships present on that occasion did not survive the war.

COUNTRY: Great Britain	
TYPE: Destroyer	
LAUNCH DATE: 1929	
CREW: 138	
DISPLACEMENT: 2022 tonnes (1990 tons)	
DIMENSIONS: 95.1m x 9.8m x 3.7m (312ft x 32ft 3in x 12ft 3in)	
RANGE: 4630km (2500nm)	
MAIN ARMAMENT: Four 120mm (4.7in) guns; eight 533mm (21in) torpedo tubes	
POWERPLANT: Twin shaft geared turbines	
PERFORMANCE: 35 knots	

During World War I, the Royal Navy had initiated large destroyer construction programmes, which meant no new vessels of this type were authorized until 1924. Prototypes were built by Britain's two foremost destroyer builders, Thorneycroft and Yarrow, based on the most recent design available, but with higher speed, all-steel bridges and a wider radius of action. From them stemmed the A class, which introduced quadruple torpedo tubes and had full gun shields. *Ardent* was one of a class of eight units with which the Royal Navy began a new era of destroyer construction, after a lapse of eight years from the end of World War I.

Victims of German guns

The class introduced quadruple torpedo tubes and had full shields for their 11.9cm (4.7in) guns. *Ardent* and her sister ship *Acasta* were sunk in June 1940 by the German battlecruisers *Scharnhorst* and *Gneisenau* while escorting the aircraft carrier *Glorious*, which also fell victim to the German guns. Apart from the above-named, the ships of this class were the *Achates* (lost 31 December 1942), *Acheron* (lost 17 December 1940), *Active*, *Antelope*, *Anthony* and *Arrow*. Two more ships of this design served with the Royal Canadian Navy as the *Saguenay* and *Skeena*. The latter ran aground on the coast of Iceland in 1944.

HMS *Ardent* was one of a flotilla of eight vessels. Two similar boats were also built for the Royal Canadian Navy, with strengthened hulls for ice navigation.

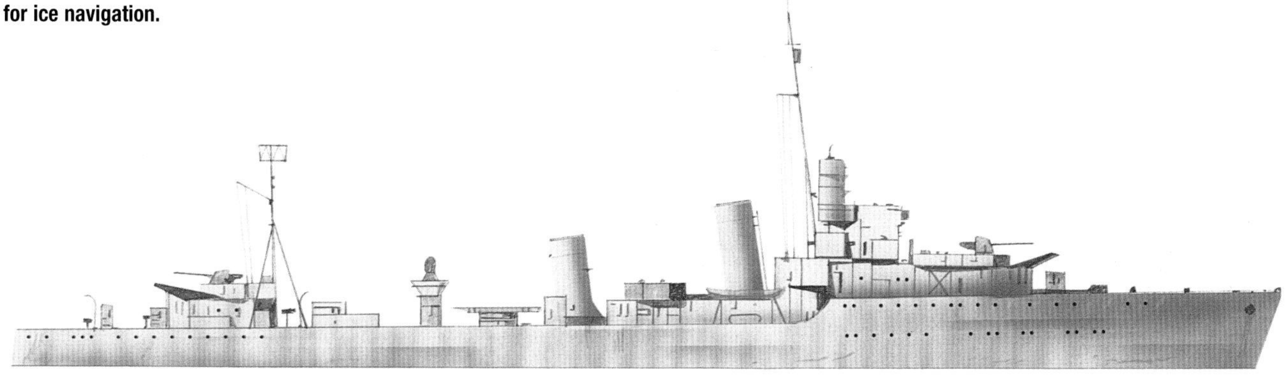

Ersh

The Ersh–class boats were notable as the first submarines of mainly Soviet design, previous craft having been brought into service with foreign assistance.

COUNTRY: Soviet Union
TYPE: Attack submarine
LAUNCH DATE: 16 November 1931
CREW: 45
DISPLACEMENT: Surfaced: 595 tonnes (586 tons), submerged: 713 tonnes (702 tons)
DIMENSIONS: 58.5m x 6.2m x 4.2m (192ft x 20ft 4in x 13ft 9in)
SURFACE RANGE: 11,112km (6000nm) at 8 knots
ARMAMENT: Six 533mm (21in) torpedo tubes, two 45mm (1.8in) guns
POWERPLANT: Twin screw diesel engines, electric motors
PERFORMANCE: Surfaced: 12.5 knots, submerged: 8.5 knots

***Ersh*'s hunting ground was the Baltic, a relatively shallow sea where submarines can fall foul of underwater obstacles in coastal waters.**

The Ersh (Pike) class of 88 boats, to which *Shch-303* belonged, were single-hull coastal submarines with a maximum diving depth of 90m (295ft). The submarines of this basic design were constructed from 1933 until after the end of World War II. Changes made in the course of building resulted in increased tonnage and a redesign of the conning tower. The progressively improved variants were designated Series III, V, VII, VIII, X and XII. Many carried the same names as submarines that served in the Tsarist era; many were named after fish. During World War II 32 were lost, but the survivors stayed in service until the mid-1950s. *Shch-303* operated in the Baltic, which was heavily mined and where most of the losses occurred; some of the Russian boats were sunk by Finnish submarines.

Shch-303 was decommissioned and scrapped at Kronstadt in 1958. Her conning tower is preserved as a memorial ashore.

Danger from Russian submarines

The Russian submarines presented a great danger to the Germans, despite inflated claims of shipping sunk, and had to be guarded against at a cost that was unwelcome when German naval forces were badly needed elsewhere. *Shch-303*'s captain, I.V. Travkin, claimed to have sunk two large vessels in the Baltic, but the claim was never substantiated. *Shch-303* survived the war and was scrapped in 1958.

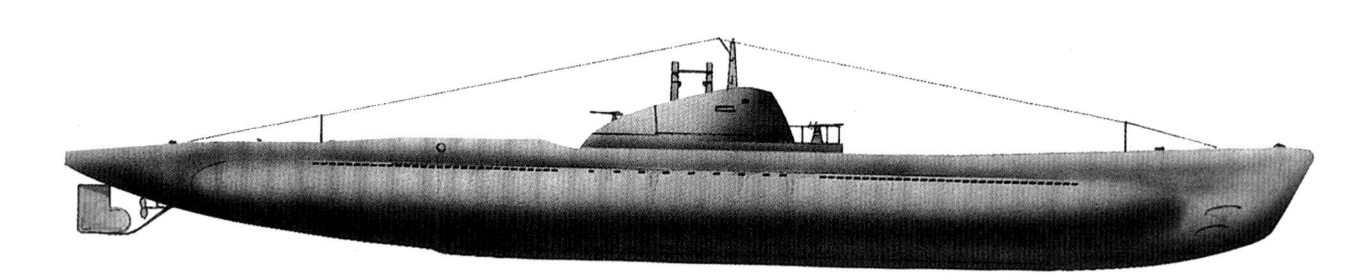

Folgore

When the fascist dictator Benito Mussolini came to power in Italy after World War I he allocated funds for the building of new vessels like *Folgore*.

COUNTRY: Italy	
TYPE: Destroyer	
LAUNCH DATE: 26 April 1931	
CREW: 175	
DISPLACEMENT: 2123 tonnes (2090 tons)	
DIMENSIONS: 96m x 9.2m x 3.3m (315ft x 30ft 2in x 10ft 10in)	
RANGE: 6840km (3693nm)	
MAIN ARMAMENT: Four 119mm (4.7in) guns; six 533mm (21in) torpedo tubes	
POWERPLANT: Twin screw turbines	
PERFORMANCE: 38.8 knots	

Like other Italian destroyers built during the 1930s, the *Folgore* was a very attractive ship. She saw much active service in World War II.

Italy's main rival for naval supremacy in the Mediterranean during the 1930s was France, with whom she was in a state of high tension over the expansion of Italy's North African colony of Libya. France saw the Italian Navy as a threat to her lines of communication with North Africa, while Italy viewed the substantial French Navy as a direct challenge to her own power and ambition. At Washington in 1922 the two countries had agreed to maintain parity in their respective battleship and cruiser strengths. This did not apply to smaller vessels, so Italy launched a large destroyer-construction programme.

Speedy minelayers

Folgore was one of a class of four fast destroyers developed from the earlier Freccia class, with a narrower beam than before, which reduced hull drag and ensured a high sustained speed. There was less internal storage space, which reduced the weapons, equipment and fuel they carried. All four ships had their armament upgraded, and were eventually modified to carry 52 mines. They were popular minelaying vessels, their high speed enabling them to transit to and from the mining area quickly, leaving them less vulnerable to detection and interception. The whole class saw extensive active service during World War II. Three were sunk in action, including *Folgore*, which was destroyed by British cruisers in December 1942.

The ships of the Folgore class were the equals of their French and British counterparts, but were never handled with the same expertise.

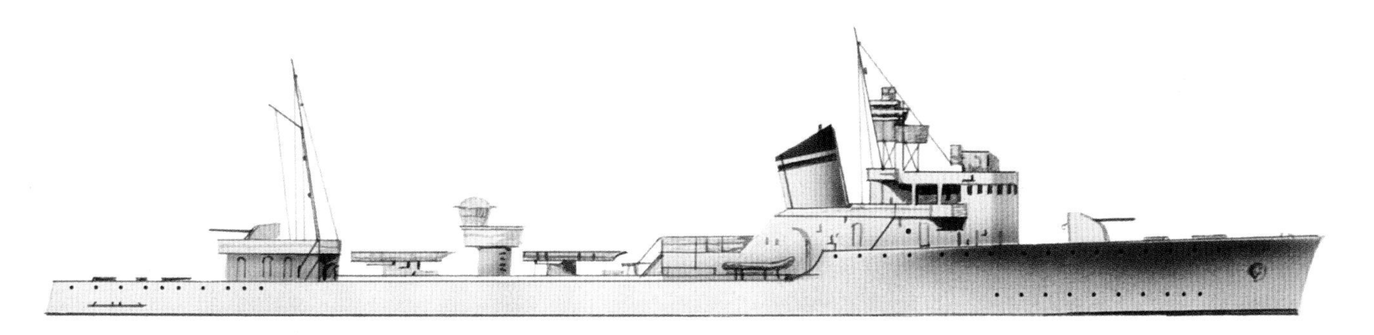

Duncan

HMS *Duncan* saw plenty of action during World War II and, unlike many others of her type, was fortunate to survive the conflict.

COUNTRY:	Great Britain
TYPE:	Destroyer
LAUNCH DATE:	7 July 1932
CREW:	145
DISPLACEMENT:	1973 tonnes (1942 tons)
DIMENSIONS:	100m x 10m x 4m (329ft x 32ft 10in x 12ft 10in)
RANGE:	2778km (1500nm)
MAIN ARMAMENT:	Four 120mm (4.7in) guns
POWERPLANT:	Twin screw, turbines
PERFORMANCE:	35.5 knots

The D-class destroyers, including HMS *Duncan*, were hard-working warships and were deployed to stations all around the globe.

HMS *Duncan* was one of 14 C- and D-class destroyers laid down in 1931 and 1932 respectively. The C-class boats served in the Western Approaches and North Atlantic, while the D class were all transferred to the Mediterranean from China when war broke out.

Destroyer leader

Duncan was fitted out as a destroyer leader and spent two years on the Gibraltar station as a part of Force H, escorting Mediterranean convoys, and taking part in the Allied landings at Diego Suarez, Madagascar, before being transferred to the Western Approaches. In May 1943, while on convoy escort duty, she helped to sink the U381 and damaged the U707. She was scrapped in November 1945. Nine of the other ships in her class were lost during the war, including three of the five that were transferred to the Royal Canadian Navy (RCN). Of the other vessels in *Duncan*'s class, *Duchess* and *Daring* returned to home waters and *Delight* joined the Home Fleet. *Diana* was transferred to the RCN, only to be lost on her first commission as RCN *Margaree* in October 1940. Others in the class went from the Mediterranean to the South Atlantic and then back to the Mediterranean. *Decoy* spent some months with the Eastern Fleet before transferring to the RCN, who used her on convoy escort duty. *Fraser* was lost in a collision off the Gironde; *Ottawa* (ex-*Crusader*) was sunk by the U-91 in the Gulf of St Lawrence; *Dainty* was bombed off Tobruk; *Daring* was sunk by the U-23; *Defender*, *Delight* and *Diamond* were all lost to air attack; while *Duchess* sank after colliding with the battleship Barham in the North Channel.

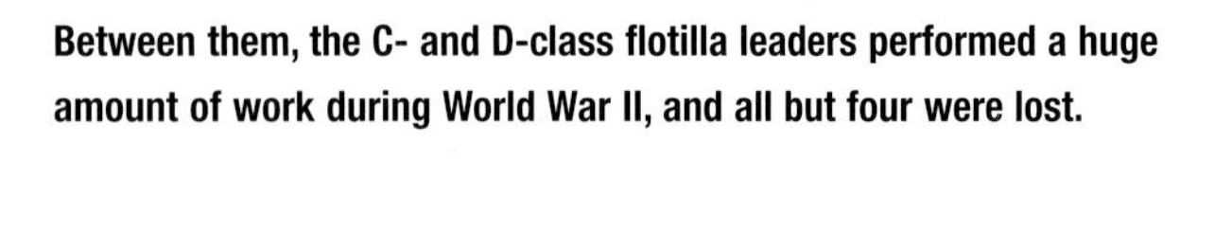

Between them, the C- and D-class flotilla leaders performed a huge amount of work during World War II, and all but four were lost.

Admiral Graf Spee

The *Admiral Graf Spee* burst into the world's headlines in December 1939, when she was driven into Montevideo by a force of British cruisers. She was ordered to be scuttled by her skipper, Captain Langsdorff.

COUNTRY: Germany
TYPE: Battleship
LAUNCH DATE: 30 June 1934
CREW: 926
DISPLACEMENT: 10,160 tonnes (10,000 tons)
DIMENSIONS: 186m x 20.6m x 7.2m (610ft 3in x 67ft 7in x 23ft 7in)
RANGE: 37,040km (20,000nm) at 15 knots
ARMAMENT: Six 279mm (11in), eight 150mm (6in) guns
POWERPLANT: Eight sets of MAN diesels, two shafts
PERFORMANCE: 26 knots

The *Admiral Graf Spee* was designed as a commerce raider, a role in which she proved very effective until she was hunted down.

Limited by the 1919 Treaty of Versailles to a maximum displacement of 10,200 tonnes (10,039 tons), Germany produced the cleverly designed 'pocket' battleship. Great savings were achieved by using electric welding and light alloys in the hull. Even before the outbreak of war, the *Graf Spee* was well known in naval circles. She was the flagship of the German fleet, and her pre-war activities had included participation in the multi-national Non-Intervention patrol off Spain during that civil war. In May 1937 she represented the German Navy at Spithead during the naval review to mark the coronation of King George VI. She had an experienced crew under the command of Captain Hans Langsdorff, who treated captured merchant seamen with great respect and courtesy. She sank her first merchantman, the British steamer *Clement*, on 30 September 1939.

Powerful armoured cruiser

The ship was scuttled off Montevideo after engaging three British cruisers, *Exeter*, *Ajax* and *Achilles*, in the Battle of the River Plate in December 1939. This ship was officially classified as being an 'armoured ship' by the Germans, though it was popularly referred to as being a 'pocket' battleship. Neither term is strictly correct, as she was an armoured cruiser of an exceptionally powerful type.

Admiral Graf Spee **(shown here), and her two sister ships, *Deutschland* and *Admiral Scheer*, were intended primarily as commerce raiders.**

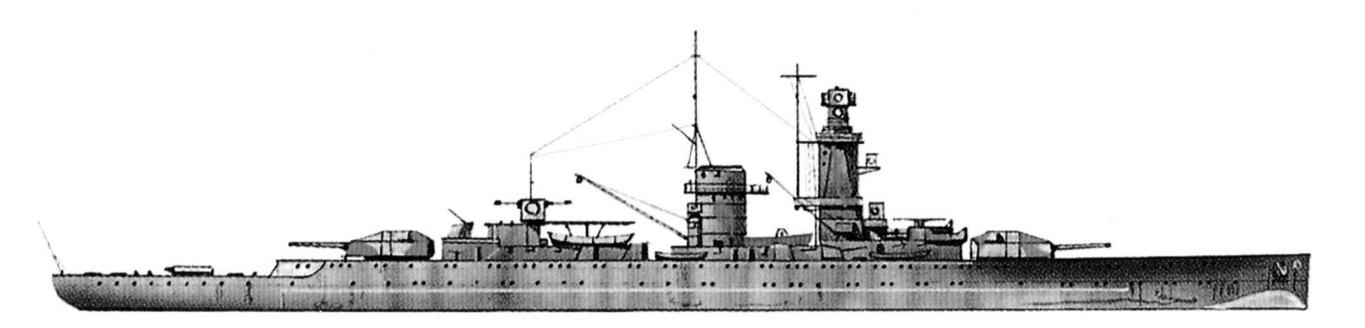

Electra

'HMS *Electra* attacked through the smoke and was seen no more.' Such was the cryptic signal that told of the end of this gallant destroyer and her crew.

COUNTRY: Great Britain	
TYPE: Destroyer	
LAUNCH DATE: 15 February 1934	
CREW: 145	
DISPLACEMENT: 1397 tonnes (1375 tons)	
DIMENSIONS: 100.2m x 10.3m x 2.6m (329ft x 33ft 9in x 8ft 6in)	
RANGE: 3889km (2100nm)	
MAIN ARMAMENT: Four 120mm (4.7in) guns; eight 533mm (21in) torpedo tubes	
POWERPLANT: Two-shaft geared turbines	
PERFORMANCE: 35.5 knots	

The flotilla leader HMS *Electra* was one of three E-class destroyers transferred to the Eastern Fleet in 1942.

Launched on February 1934, HMS *Electra* was one of nine E-class destroyers. She saw initial action off Norway in April 1940, and a year later, as part of the escort to the battleship *Prince of Wales*, she took participated in the hunt for the German battleship *Bismarck*. In October 1941, together with the destroyer *Express*, she accompanied the *Prince of Wales* to Singapore, and was present when the battleship and the battlecruiser *Repulse* were sunk off Malaya by Japanese air attack on 10 December 1941.

Attacked through a smokescreen

On 27 February 1942 she formed part of a force of British, Dutch and US warships that intercepted Japanese forces in the Java Sea. In a confused short-range action with eight enemy destroyers and the cruiser *Naka*, the *Electra* attacked through a smokescreen and was seen no more. The outcome of the Battle of the Java Sea ended any Allied hopes of contesting the Japanese invasion of South-east Asia. The Royal Navy's assets in the theatre were reduced to the old light cruisers *Danae* and *Dragon* and the destroyers *Scout* and *Tenedos*, which, accompanied by the Australian cruiser HMS *Hobart*, had set out from the Sunda Strait for Colombo on 28 February, picking up refugees en route. Another British destroyer, HMS *Stronghold,* was sunk by enemy warships on 2 March during the withdrawal from Java, together with HMAS *Yarra*.

In the Battle of the Java Sea, HMS *Electra* formed part of an Allied force under the command of the Dutch Admiral Karel Doorman.

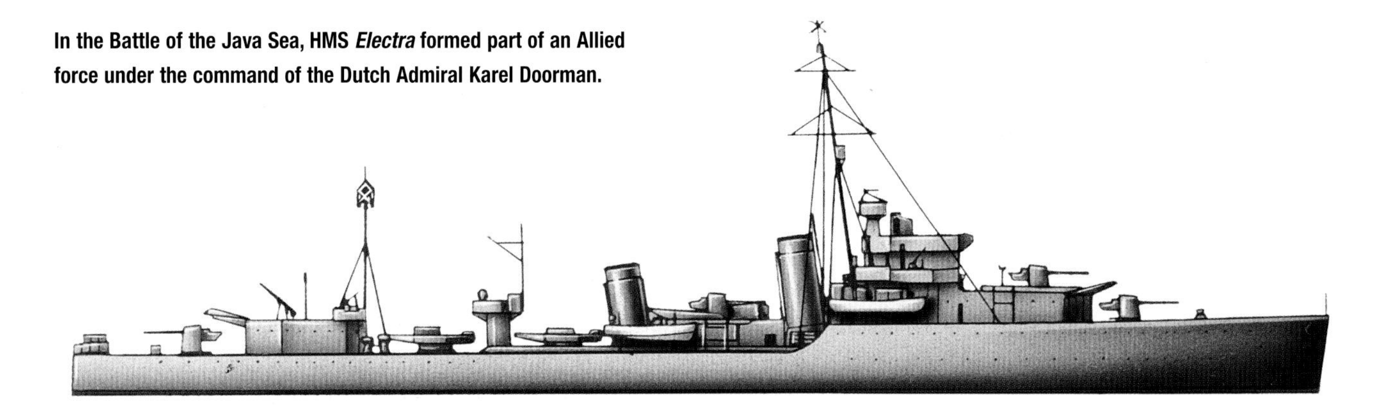

Dunkerque

***Dunkerque* was the flagship of Admiral Gensoul, whose flat refusal to consider British requests to join forces precipitated the attack on his warships at Oran.**

Based on the British Nelson class battleships, *Dunkerque* was the first French warship to be laid down after the Washington Treaty of 1922. She was the culmination of a series of design studies that responded to the German Deutschland class of the 1930s. A hangar and a catapult were provided for the four scout planes she was to carry.

The hunt for the *Admiral Graf Spee*

In October 1939 she joined the Royal Navy in the hunt for the German pocket battleship *Admiral Graf Spee*. She did convoy escort duty until the surrender of France, and

COUNTRY: France
TYPE: Battleship
LAUNCH DATE: 2 October 1935
CREW: 1431
DISPLACEMENT: 36,068 tonnes (35,500 tons)
DIMENSIONS: 214.5m x 31m x 8.6m (703ft 9in x 102ft 3in x 28ft 6in)
RANGE: 13,897km (7500nm) at 15 knots
ARMAMENT: 16 127mm (5in), eight 330mm (13in) guns
POWERPLANT: Quadruple screw turbines
PERFORMANCE: 29.5 knots

The *Dunkerque* was never repaired after suffering severe damage in WWII, her hulk being broken up in 1958.

in July 1940 was damaged by British warships at Mers-el-Kebir and by a torpedo attack three days later, with the loss of 210 lives. The torpedo attack was carried out by Fairey Swordfish aircraft from the carrier *Ark Royal*. She was not actually hit by any torpedoes, but four of them hit the auxiliary vessel *Terre Neuve*, lying alongside *Dunkerque* with a cargo of depth charges. These exploded and ripped open the battleship's side, putting her out of action.

She was refloated and moved to Toulon harbour in 1942, where she was scuttled in November after German occupation of Vichy France.

Conyngham

The Mahan class of US destroyers, to which the USS *Conyngham* belonged, gave excellent service in the early part of the Pacific war, especially in the waters around the embattled island of Guadalcanal in 1942.

COUNTRY: USA
TYPE: Destroyer
LAUNCH DATE: 14 September 1935
CREW: 250
DISPLACEMENT: 1417 tonnes (1395 tons)
DIMENSIONS: 104m x 10.4m x 2.69m (341.25ft x 34.16ft x 8.83ft)
RANGE: 6482km (3500nm)
Main ARMAMENT: Five single 127mm DP guns; two quadruple 533mm (21in) torpedo tubes
POWERPLANT: Two sets of geared steam turbines
PERFORMANCE: 36.5 knots

The *Mahans,* of which *USS Fanning* was the last, introduced high-pressure boilers – used by most US warships for the next two decades.

At the time of the Japanese attack on Pearl Harbor on 7 December 1941 the US Navy had 171 destroyers in commission, over one-third of these World War I vintage; the remainder were all built after 1932. These were the Farragut, Mahan and Craven classes, which were successive modifications of a basic design with an armament of 5in guns and torpedo tubes. All US destroyers built in the 1930s had excellent range.

Losses and destruction

Launched in September 1935, the USS *Conyngham* was one of the Mahan class of American destroyers, closely related to the preceding Farragut class. Of the 18 ships in the class, six were lost in World War II. *Cassin* and *Downes* were virtually destroyed at Pearl Harbor but were later rebuilt; the USS *Tucker* survived the attack on Pearl Harbor but was lost in August 1942; the *Cushing* was sunk by Japanese gunfire and torpedoes off Guadalcanal on 13 November 1942; the *Preston* was sunk off Guadalcanal by a Japanese battle group on 14 November 1942; the *Perkins* went down in the Southwest Pacific on 29 November 1943; the *Mahan* was lost on 7 December 1944; and the *Reid* was lost on 11 December 1944. Another vessel, the *Lamson*, was expended at the Bikini atomic bomb tests in 1946, and the *Conyngham* herself was sunk as a target vessel on 2 July 1948.

During 1941, *Conyngham* and other ships of her class had their tripod foremast replaced by a pole, as pictured here.

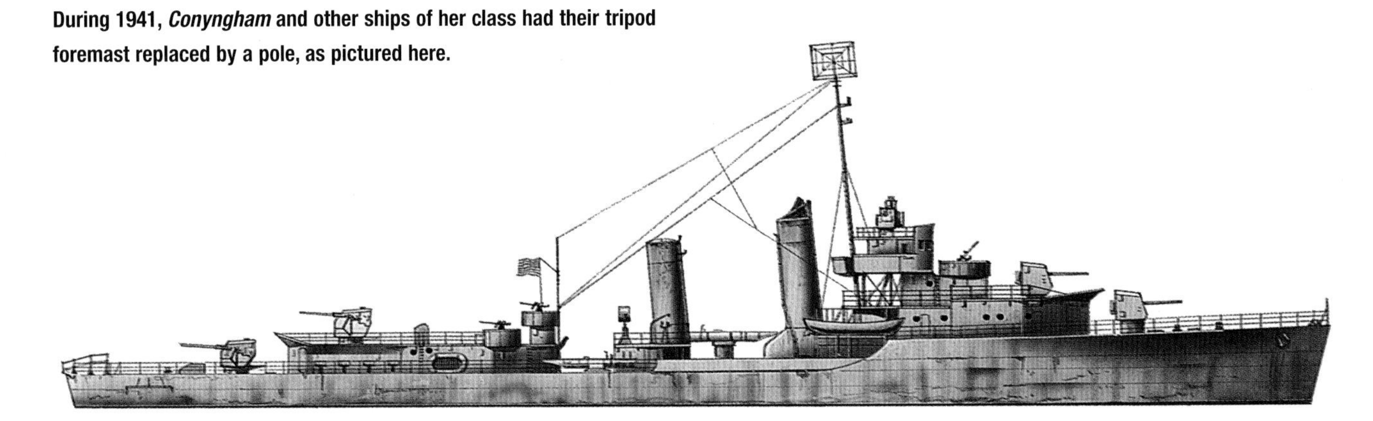

Leberecht Maas

The *Leberecht Maas* was the first of the 1934-type destroyers. She was an early casualty of the war, as were several others in the German destroyer forces.

COUNTRY: Germany
TYPE: Destroyer
LAUNCH DATE: 18 August 1935
CREW: 315
DISPLACEMENT: 3211 tonnes (3160 tons)
DIMENSIONS: 119m x 11.3m x 3.8m (390ft 5in x 37ft 1in x 12ft 6in)
RANGE: 8135km (4393nm)
MAIN ARMAMENT: Five single 127mm (5in) guns; two quadruple 533mm (21in) torpedo tubes; up to 60 mines
POWERPLANT: Two-shaft geared turbines
PERFORMANCE: 30 knots

At the outbreak of World War II the Kriegsmarine had a considerable destroyer force with modern types such as the *Leberecht Maas.*

At the start of World War II, the Kriegsmarine was armed with two classes of destroyer; the Diether von Roeder class, comprising six ships, and the Leberecht Maass class of 16. The two classes were very similar in size and displacement, although the von Roeder class, the last of the pre-war destroyers, had a superior performance. All German destroyers in the North Sea area were under the command of Admiral Densch's Reconnaissance Forces.

Lack of freeboard

The Type 34 or Maass class were the first German destroyers to be built since World War I. Of conventional layout, their only major problem was lack of freeboard, which had disagreeable consequences in heavy seas. All 16 ships were launched between 1937 and 1939. Five were sunk by Royal Navy destroyer forces in the Second Battle of Narvik in April 1940. Of the remainder, *Leberecht Maass* and *Max Schulz* were mined and sunk in the North Sea on 22 February 1940; *Hermann Schoemann* was sunk in Arctic waters by the RN cruiser HMS *Edinburgh* on 2 May 1942; *Bruno Heinemann* was mined and sunk in the English Channel on 25 January 1942; *Friedrich Eckoldt* was sunk in the Barents Sea by the RN cruisers *Jamaica* and *Sheffield* on 31 December 1942; one was broken up post-war in the UK; and two went to the Soviet Union in 1946.

The Leberecht Maas-class vessels were an attempt to build a 'strategic' destroyer capable of ocean-going operations.

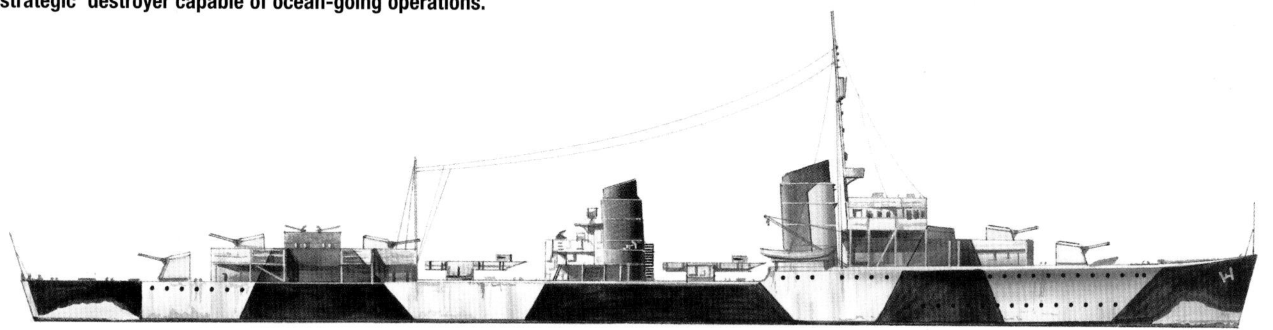

Enterprise

The name of the aircraft carrier USS *Enterprise* became synonymous with the Battle of Midway in June 1942, when her aircraft dealt out enormous punishment to the Japanese fleet but suffered terrible casualties.

The *Enterprise* was present at all the major Pacific fleet engagements of World War II. She went to the breaker's yard in 1958.

COUNTRY: USA	
TYPE: Aircraft carrier	
LAUNCH DATE: 3 October 1936	
CREW: 2175	
DISPLACEMENT: 25,908 tonnes (25,500 tons)	
DIMENSIONS: 246.7m x 26.2m x 7.9m (809ft 6in x 86ft x 26ft)	
RANGE: 21,600km (12,000nm) at 12 knots	
ARMAMENT: Eight 127mm (5in) guns	
POWERPLANT: Quadruple screw turbines	
PERFORMANCE: 37.5 knots	

Early *Enterprise* designs had a flush deck, but this was thought to pose a smoke threat to landing aircraft, and an island structure to carry funnel uptakes and provide control centres was devised. The aircraft hangars were light structures independent from the hull that could be closed off with rolling shutters. *Enterprise* was refitted in 1942 after action at the Battle of Midway, during which her dive-bombers helped sink three Japanese carriers.

The cost of Midway

The US victory at Midway was achieved at terrible cost. The *Enterprise*'s air group, attacking the Japanese carrier *Soryu* with 12 TBDs of torpedo-bomber squadron VT-3 and 17 SBD dive-bombers of VB-3, escorted by six F4F Wildcats of VF-3, suffered awful punishment. Only five TBDs survived to make their attacks, and three of these were shot down. Of the 41 TBDs launched by *Enterprise* and other US carriers, only six returned, and one of these ran out of fuel and ditched. *Enterprise*'s World War II battle honours included Guadalcanal, Eastern Solomons, Gilbert Islands, Kwajalein, Eniwetok, the Truk raid, Hollandia, Saipan, the Battle of the Philippine Sea, Palau, Leyte, Luzon, Taiwan, the China coast, Iwo Jima and Okinawa.

She received five bomb hits and survived two attacks by kamikazes, yet was sold in 1958, despite efforts to preserve her as a memorial.

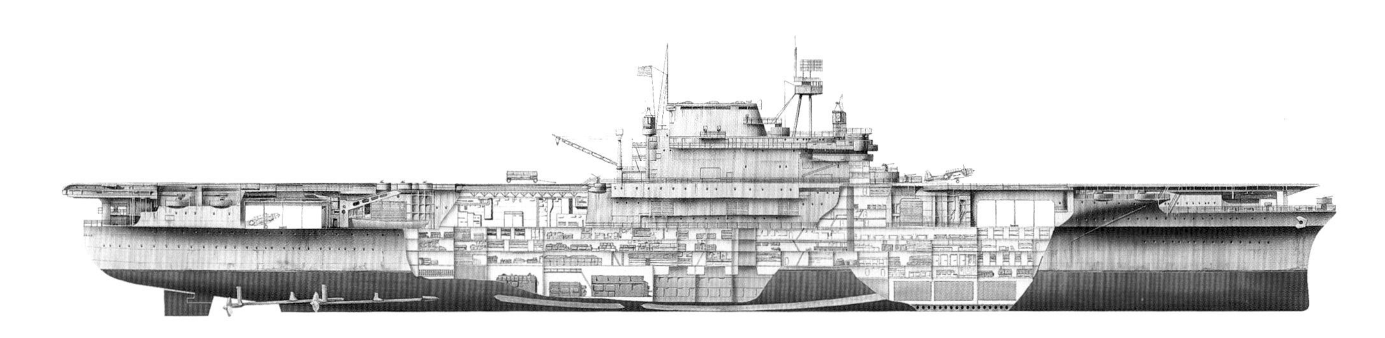

Gneisenau

In 1941 the *Gneisenau, Scharnhorst* and the mighty battleship *Bismarck* were to have formed a powerful battle group to operate against Allied convoys in the Atlantic. They were thwarted by the RAF and the Royal Navy.

COUNTRY: Germany
TYPE: Battleship
LAUNCH DATE: 8 December 1936
CREW: 1840
DISPLACEMENT: 39,522 tonnes (38,900 tons)
DIMENSIONS: 226m x 30m x 9m (741ft 6in x 98ft 5in x 30ft)
RANGE: 16,306km (8800nm) at 18 knots
ARMAMENT: 14 104mm (4.1in), 12 150mm (5.9in), nine 279mm (11in) guns
POWERPLANT: Triple screw turbines, with diesels for cruising
PERFORMANCE: 32 knots

The *Gneisenau* was to have formed part of a powerful task force that might have destroyed Britain's vital Atlantic lifelines.

Both launched in 1936, *Gneisenau* and her sister *Scharnhorst* were completed with straight stems, but the bows were later lengthened. Both vessels served in World War II, attacking British commerce and sinking the British aircraft carrier *Glorious*. Both ships received damage from air attacks in 1941 while in Brest harbour, and in February 1942, with the cruiser *Prinz Eugen*, they broke out and made an epic dash across the English Channel for the north German ports. *Gneisenau* reached Kiel only to be damaged in an RAF bombing raid two weeks later, after which she was moved to Gdynia (Gdansk). She was decommissioned in July 1942 and her turrets were removed for coastal defence. A refit was abandoned in 1943 and her hulk was sunk as a blockship at Gdynia in March 1945. Salvaged by the Russians, she was broken up in 1947–51.

Torpedoed in Brest harbour

The honour of preventing *Gneisenau's* breakout into the Atlantic in 1941 went to a single RAF crew. On 6 April 1941, a Bristol Beaufort torpedo-bomber of No. 22 Squadron RAF, piloted by Flying Officer Kenneth Campbell, flew into Brest harbour to make its torpedo run at mast height through intense flak. Campbell was eventually brought down, but not before he had released his torpedo at a range of 450m (500yds). The torpedo exploded on the *Gneisenau's* stern below the waterline, putting the cruiser out of action for months. Campbell was posthumously awarded the Victoria Cross.

The British classified the *Gneisenau* as a battlecruiser, but the Germans called it a battleship – probably a more accurate description.

Ark Royal

The Germans claimed to have sunk the aircraft carrier *Ark Royal* several times, even producing illustrations of her sinking after an air attack in the North Sea. But it was not until November 1941 that she met her end.

COUNTRY: Great Britain	
TYPE: Aircraft carrier	
LAUNCH DATE: 13 April 1937	
CREW: 1580	
DISPLACEMENT: 28,164 tonnes (27,720 tons)	
DIMENSIONS: 243.8m x 28.9m x 8.5m (800ft x 94ft 9in x 27ft 9in)	
RANGE: 14,119km (7620nm) at 20 knots	
ARMAMENT: 16 114mm (4.5in) guns, 60 aircraft	
POWERPLANT: Triple shaft geared turbines	
PERFORMANCE: 31 knots	

The *Ark Royal* was a highly publicized British aircraft carrier in the early part of World War II, and thus a primary target for the Germans.

Ark Royal was the first large purpose-built aircraft carrier to be constructed for the Royal Navy, with a long flight deck some 18m (60ft) above the deep-water load line. The aircraft carrier's full complement was 60 aircraft, although she never actually carried this many as such a load would have reduced her fighting capability. During her war operations, she took part in the Norwegian campaign of 1940 and was then transferred to the Mediterranean Theatre, where she joined 'Force H' at Gibraltar. In May 1941 one of her Swordfish aircraft torpedoed the German battleship *Bismarck*, destroying the warship's steering gear, which led to her being sunk by the British Fleet. On 10 November 1941, *Ark Royal* and another aircraft carrier, *Argus*, set out from Gibraltar to a flying-off point 725km (450 miles) from the besieged island of Malta, and on the 12th they launched 37 Hurricanes, of which 34 reached the island together with seven Blenheim bombers.

Ark Royal is hit

As the carriers made their homeward run, *Ark Royal* was hit by a torpedo, one of a salvo of four fired by the German submarine U-81, near her starboard boiler room. Only one crew member lost his life in the attack and valiant efforts were made to save the carrier, but she sank under tow only 40km (25 miles) from Gibraltar.

The *Ark Royal* was the bearer of a proud name, first used on a vessel in the navy of Queen Elizabeth I in 1587.

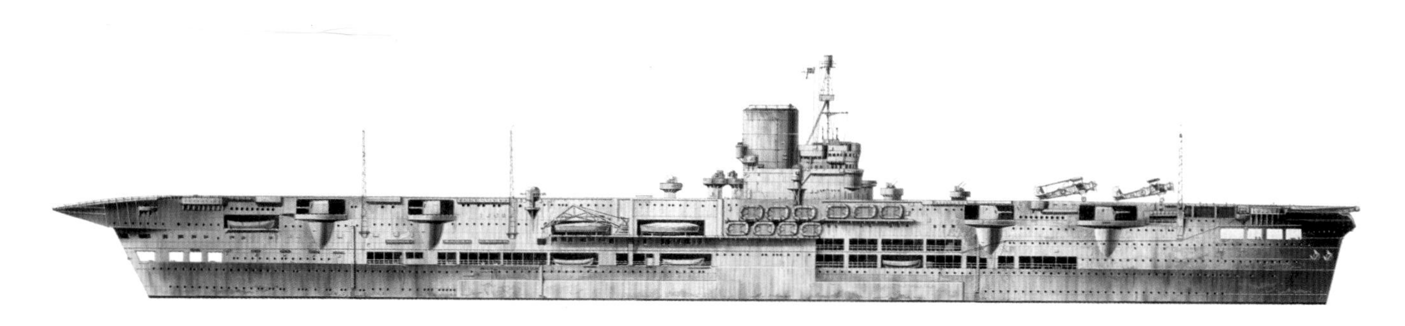

Brin

The *Brin* was one of the best-known Italian submarines of World War II, thanks to her role in helping to train Allied anti-submarine forces after Italy's surrender.

COUNTRY: Italy	
TYPE: Attack submarine	
LAUNCH DATE: 3 April 1938	
CREW: 58	
DISPLACEMENT: Surfaced: 1032 tonnes (1016 tons), submerged: 1286 tonnes (1266 tons)	
DIMENSIONS: 70m x 7m x 4.2m (231ft 4in x 22ft 6in x 13ft 6in)	
SURFACE RANGE: 18,530km (10,000nm) at 10 knots	
ARMAMENT: Eight 533mm (21in) torpedo tubes, one 100mm (3.9in) gun	
POWERPLANT: Twin screw diesel engines, two electric motors	
PERFORMANCE: Surfaced: 17 knots, submerged: 8 knots	

The *Brin* pictured at speed on the surface during exercises with Allied naval aircraft in the Indian Ocean, 1944.

Brin (named after the Italian naval engineer Benedetto Brin) was one of a class of long-range submarines with a partial double hull developed from the Archimede class. A feature of the Brin class was their tall conning tower. This caused some embarrassment when, in June 1940, Benito Mussolini declared war on Britain and France and ordered some Italian submarines to set up a base at Bordeaux. During this period, the Italians had more submarines operating in the Atlantic than did the Germans, but the tall conning towers of the Italian boats made them easy to spot on the surface and as a consequence they registered few successes against the Allied convoys.

The *Brin*, sporting the unusual camouflage scheme used during Aegean operations in 1941–42, was eventually discarded in 1948.

Based in French Atlantic ports

Brin was active from the start of Italy's involvement in World War II, first forming part of a submarine squadron covering the approaches to the Aegean Sea. In 1941, as part of an Italian submarine group based on French Atlantic ports, she operated against Allied convoys in the sea area west of Gibraltar. Following the Italian armistice in September 1943, under Allied command, she transferred to Ceylon and was used to train Allied anti-submarine warfare forces in the Indian Ocean.

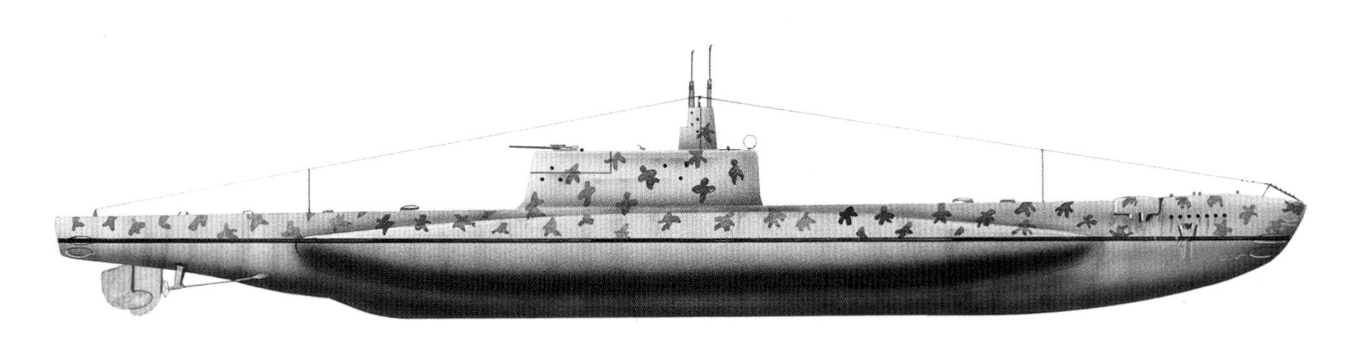

Kelly

The K-class destroyer HMS *Kelly* was destined to become a famous ship with a famous captain, Lord Louis Mountbatten. The exploits of the ship and her crew were made famous in the film *In Which We Serve*.

COUNTRY: Great Britain
TYPE: Destroyer
LAUNCH DATE: 25 October 1938
CREW: 218
DISPLACEMENT: 1722 tonnes (1695 tons)
DIMENSIONS: 108.7m x 10.9m x 2.75m (356ft 6in x 35ft 9in x 9ft)
RANGE: 4444km (2400nm)
MAIN ARMAMENT: Six 119mm (4.7in) guns
POWERPLANT: Two-shaft geared turbines
PERFORMANCE: 36 knots

Having seen distinguished service in the early months of the war, the *Kelly* felt the full fury of German air attack off Crete in 1941.

Launched in October 1938, HMS *Kelly* was one of a class that marked a change in British destroyer design. The first single-funnelled class this century, the J, K and I classes adopted the guns and the turrets used in the big vessels of the Tribal class, but mounted on a more easily built hull. The six 119mm (4.7in) Mk XII guns had a maximum elevation of 40 degrees, leaving air defence to the quadruple two-pounder 'pom-pom' abaft the funnel. This weakness was highlighted by the loss early in the war of several vessels, including *Kelly*, to air attack, particularly dive-bombing. *Kelly* was active in the closing stages of the Norwegian campaign, covering the evacuation of Allied troops from Norwegian harbours.

Of the 17 K- and J-class destroyers that served in the Mediterranean, no fewer than 12 were lost through enemy action.

Damaged by a torpedo

On 10 May 1940, during a sortie into the Skagerrak with six other destroyers and the cruiser *Birmingham*, she was damaged by a torpedo from the German MTB S31 and had to be towed to Newcastle-upon-Tyne by the destroyer *Bulldog*. After repair she deployed to the Mediterranean. *Kelly* and her sister ship, *Kashmir*, were bombed and sunk by German dive-bombers off Crete on 23 May 1941.

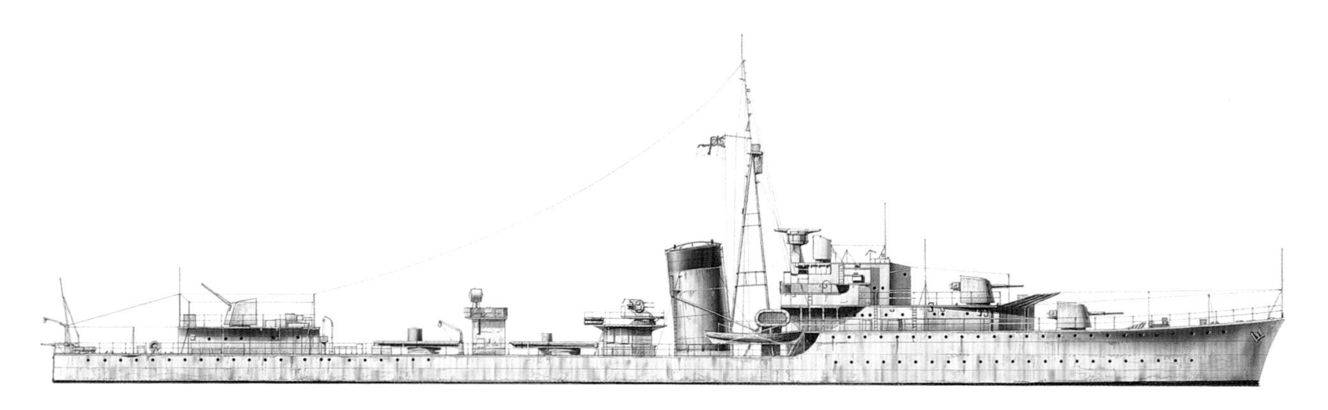

U47

The U47 and its captain, Gunther Prien, became infamous in British eyes for the sinking of the *Royal Oak*. The officer who fired the torpedoes was Oberleutnant zur Zee Endress, who went on to command the U46.

COUNTRY: Germany

TYPE: Attack submarine

LAUNCH DATE: 1938

CREW: 44

DISPLACEMENT: Surfaced: 765 tonnes (753 tons), submerged: 871 tonnes (857 tons)

DIMENSIONS: 66.5m x 6.2m x 4.7m (218ft x 20ft 3in x 15ft 6in)

SURFACE RANGE: 10,454km (5642nm) at 12 knots

ARMAMENT: Five 533mm (21in) torpedo tubes; one 88mm (3.5in) gun; one 20mm AA gun

POWERPLANT: Two-shaft diesel/electric motors

PERFORMANCE: Surfaced: 17.2 knots, submerged: 8 knots

After sinking the *Royal Oak*, the U47's crew returned home to a hero's welcome.

In strict secrecy, German naval experts had been operating in defiance of the Versailles Treaty for years before Hitler came to power. Operating from clandestine offices in the Netherlands and Spain, German submarine designers and constructors began work on undersea craft that were to serve as the prototypes of a new generation of German U-boats. Some were constructed for Finland, and one of these served as the prototype for what was to become the main operational U-boat class, the Type VII. The Type VIIB U-boat was a slightly enlarged version of the Type VIIA, with a greater range and slightly higher surface speed. The most famous boat of this class was undoubtedly the U47, under Lt Cdr Gunther Prien, who penetrated the defences of Scapa Flow and sank the 27,940-tonne (27,500-ton) battleship *Royal Oak* with three torpedo hits.

Enormous loss of life

The attack, in which 833 lives were lost, was carried out with great coolness, skill and daring, and came as a great shock to Britain. Prien returned home to a hero's welcome. He had already sunk three small merchant ships on the first day of the war, and went on to sink 27 more before U47 was sunk in the North Atlantic on 7 March 1941 by the RN corvettes *Arbutus* and *Carmellia*.

The prolific Type VIIB U-boats, of which the U47 was one example, sank a huge tonnage of Allied shipping in the early years of World War II.

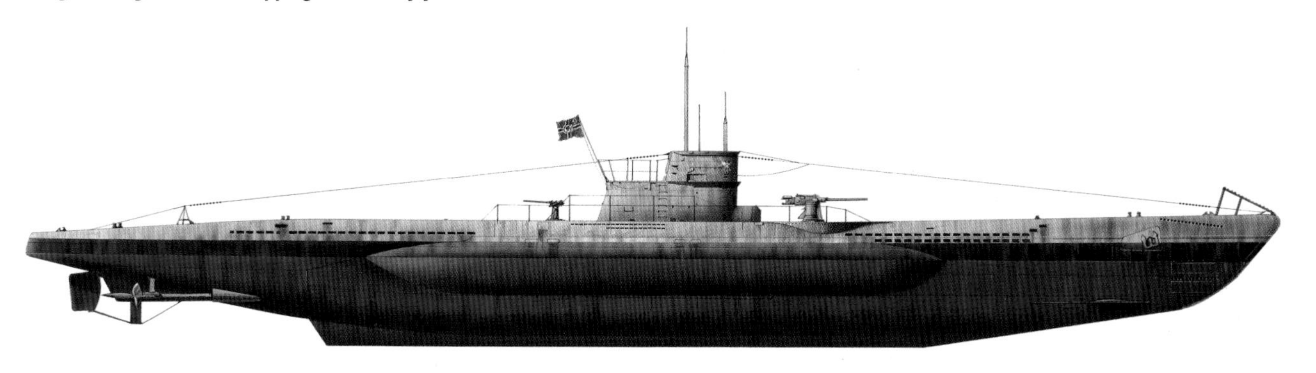

Graf Zeppelin

The *Graf Zeppelin* was intended to form the core of a powerful naval task group designed to operate in the vulnerable sea lanes of the North Atlantic.

COUNTRY: Germany
TYPE: Aircraft carrier
LAUNCH DATE: 8 December 1938
CREW: 1760 (estimated)
DISPLACEMENT: 28,540 tonnes (28,090 tons)
DIMENSIONS: 262.5m x 31.5m x 8.5m (861ft 3in x 103ft 4in x 27ft 10in)
RANGE: 14,842km (8000nm) at 19 knots
ARMAMENT: 12 104mm (4.1in), 16 150mm (5.9in) guns, 43 aircraft
POWERPLANT: Quadruple screw turbines
PERFORMANCE: 35 knots

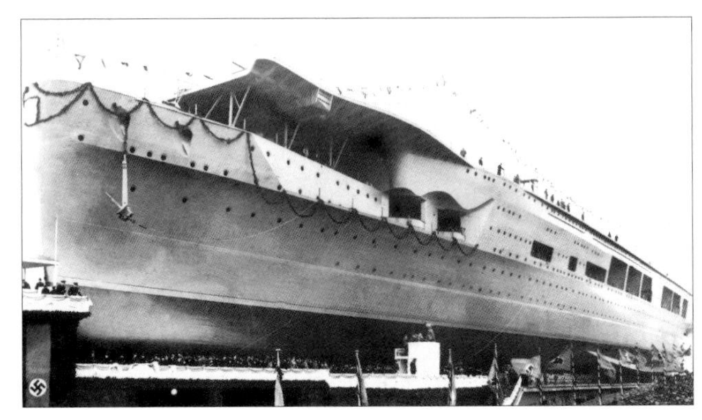

Construction of the *Graf Zeppelin* was suspended by Hitler when he believed the war was won, and was later restarted.

After World War I Germany was denied any chance of developing a carrier force as a result of restrictions imposed upon them in 1919. By 1933 Wilhelm Hadelar had prepared a basic design for a full deck carrier able to operate 40 aircraft, but lack of construction experience delayed the project. *Graf Zeppelin* was originally intended to carry an air group of 12 Ju87D dive-bombers and 30 Me109F fighters (later amended to 28 Ju87Ds and 12 Me109s). Half of a sister ship was also built; it was thought that this vessel would be named *Peter Strasser*, after the commander of the German Naval Airship Division in World War I. In 1935 work began, but completion was delayed to make way for the U-boat programme. The *Graf Zeppelin*'s construction was restarted in 1942, only to be halted.

An uncertain fate

In 1943 she was towed to Stettin on the Baltic coast, her fate uncertain. She was scuttled a few months before the end of World War II, then raised by the Russians in 1946. On 7 April 1947 she was taken under tow to Leningrad, her flight deck laden with war booty. Later, she was towed out into the Baltic and used as a floating target for Soviet warships and aircraft in August 1947. The wreck was located in the southern Baltic in 1946.

The *Graf Zeppelin* as she would have appeared had she been completed. Other carriers were also planned.

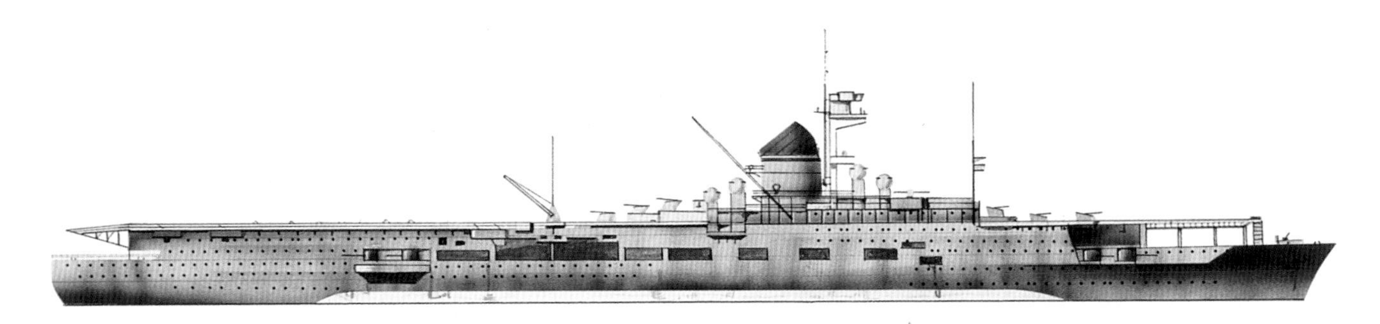

Orzel

Commissioned in February 1939, the large ocean-going Polish submarine *Orzel* (*Eagle*) was built in the De Schelde Navy Yard, Vlissingen, Holland.

COUNTRY: Poland
TYPE: Attack submarine
LAUNCH DATE: 1938
CREW: 56
DISPLACEMENT: Surfaced: 1117 tonnes (1100 tons), submerged: 1496 tonnes (1473 tons)
DIMENSIONS: 84m x 6.7m x 4m (275ft 7in x 22ft x 13ft 1in)
SURFACE RANGE: 13,300km (7169nm) at 10 knots
ARMAMENT: Twelve 550mm (21.7in) torpedo tubes, One 105mm (4in) gun
POWERPLANT: Twin screws, diesel/electric motors
PERFORMANCE: Surfaced: 15 knots, submerged: 8 knots

In September 1939 the *Orzel* and her crew made a bold and daring escape from the Baltic to join the Royal Navy.

Orzel was ordered in January 1935 and was funded by public subscription. She was a large, with excellent all-round qualities, and was Dutch-built, together with her sister ship *Wilk* (*Wolf*). Diving depth was 80m (200ft) and submerged range was 190km (102nm) at five knots. *Orzel* was commissioned in February 1939.

An adventurous voyage

Progress in completing *Orzel* was slow, partly because of pro-German sympathies among Dutch shipyard workers. After the German occupation of Czechoslovakia in March 1939 there were fears she might be sabotaged. On 2 April, she put to sea for trials, but sailed for the Baltic, still with some very surprised and indignant Dutch workers on board. With 160km (100 miles) to go she ran out of fuel, and had to be towed into Gdynia, arriving on 18 April. On 14 September 1939 the Polish submarines were ordered to break out from the Baltic and make for British ports; *Wilk* arrived on 20 September and *Orzel* (under Lt Cdr Grudzinski) on 14 October via Reval, after an adventurous voyage without charts. On 8 April 1940 *Orzel* sank two large troop transports at the start of the German invasion of Norway, but was lost in a mine barrage off the Norwegian coast on 8 June. Her sister, *Wilk*, attacked and sank a Dutch submarine in error on 20 June 1940.

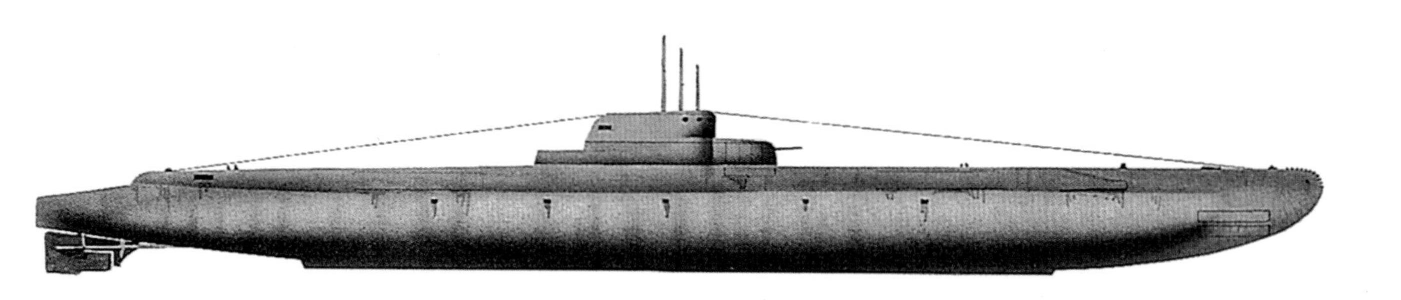

***Orzel*'s career with the Royal Navy after the collapse of Poland was brief, but her operational sorties off Norway were effective.**

Bismarck

In May 1941 the battleship *Bismarck* and her consort, the heavy cruiser *Prinz Eugen*, presented a far more serious threat to Britain's lifelines than Germany's U-boats. The Royal Navy was ordered to sink her at all cost.

COUNTRY: Germany
TYPE: Battleship
LAUNCH DATE: 14 February 1939
CREW: 2039
DISPLACEMENT: 50,955 tonnes (50,153 tons)
DIMENSIONS: 250m x 36m x 9m (823ft 6in x 118ft x 29ft 6in)
RANGE: 15,000km (8100nm) at 18 knots
ARMAMENT: Eight 380mm (15in), 12 152mm (6in) guns, six aircraft
POWERPLANT: Three shaft geared turbines
PERFORMANCE: 29 knots

The mighty *Bismarck* was to have formed the nucleus of a powerful surface action group, preying on Britain's Atlantic convoys.

In the late 1930s German naval strategy still revolved around the possibility of a future conflict in the Atlantic against a powerful French fleet, and the Munich Crisis of 1938 led Hitler (who had a very detailed knowledge of naval technology) to believe that there was also now the prospect of a naval confrontation with Britain. To be assured of naval supremacy on the high seas he needed a fleet of super-powerful battleships, two of which had already been laid down in 1936. These were the *Bismarck* and *Tirpitz*, respectively laid down as Schiff F Ersatz Hannover and Schiff G Ersatz Schleswig-Holstein. Formidably armed, displacing 41,700 tons in the case of *Bismarck* and 42,900 tons in the case of *Tirpitz*, their complement was 2400 officers and men.

Action in the Arctic

In May 1941, after completing her sea trials in the Baltic, *Bismarck* sailed for the North Atlantic accompanied by the heavy cruiser *Prinz Eugen*. Engaged by British naval forces in the Arctic, *Bismarck* sank the battlecruiser HMS *Hood* and damaged the battleship *Prince of Wales*. Having received damage herself, her commander decided to make for Brest. About 645km (400 miles) from the French coast, *Bismarck* was further damaged in a torpedo attack by British naval aircraft and sunk by British naval units, although some sources suggest that she was scuttled by her crew.

The whole appearance of the *Bismarck* exuded strength, purpose and power. Had she been able to sail with a proper battle group, she would have been invincible.

Richelieu

***Richelieu* was first in a class of four battleships planned between 1935 and 1938, but she was the only one completed in time to see action during World War I.**

COUNTRY: France
TYPE: Battleship
LAUNCH DATE: 17 January 1939
CREW: 1670
DISPLACEMENT : 47,084 tonnes (47,850 tons)
DIMENSIONS: 247.85m x 33m x 9.63m (813ft 2in x 108ft 3in x 31ft 7in)
RANGE: 10,800km (6000nm) at 12 knots
ARMAMENT: Eight 380mm (15in), nine 152mm (6in) guns
POWERPLANT: Four shaft geared turbines
PERFORMANCE: 30 knots

A fine, modern battleship, *Richelieu* served with Allied naval forces in the Indian Ocean.

Launched in March 1939, *Richelieu* was completed at Brest in June 1940 and at once sailed for the West African port of Dakar to escape capture by the Germans. In July her captain refused a British ultimatum to join the British, and a fast motor launch from the carrier HMS *Hermes* entered Dakar harbour and dropped depth charges under her stern in an attempt to put her rudder and propellers out of action. These failed to explode, and although she was later attacked by carrier aircraft from the *Hermes* their torpedoes only inflicted light damage.She joined the Allies in 1942 as part of a powerful battle group that included battleships *Valiant*, *Howe* and *Queen Elizabeth*, battlecruiser *Renown* and carriers *Victorious*, *Illustrious* and *Indomitable*. She escorted many attack sorties by the carriers on Java, Sumatra and the various enemy-held island groups in the Indian Ocean.

A substantial refit

She underwent a substantial refit in the USA in 1943, when radar and an extra 100 anti-aircraft guns were added. Joining the British Eastern Fleet in 1944, she served until the end of the war. She later operated off Indo-China during France's war there. *Richelieu* was broken up in 1964.

***Richelieu* was France's most modern battleship when France fell in June 1940, and gave good service in the Allied cause in Far Eastern waters.**

Formidable

The fleet carrier HMS *Formidable* was one of four laid down in 1937, the others being the *Illustrious*, *Indomitable* and *Victorious*. All had armoured flight decks, which saved them from disaster on several occasions.

HMS *Formidable* was the second member of the Illustrious class of fleet carrier, the third and last being HMS *Victorious*.

COUNTRY: Great Britain	
TYPE: Aircraft carrier	
LAUNCH DATE: 17 August 1939	
CREW: 1997	
DISPLACEMENT: 28,661 tonnes (28,210 tons)	
DIMENSIONS: 226.7m x 29.1m x 8.5m (743ft 9in x 95ft 9in x 28ft)	
RANGE: 20,383km (11,000nm) at 14 knots	
ARMAMENT: 16 112mm (4.5in) guns, 36 aircraft	
POWERPLANT: Triple screw turbines	
PERFORMANCE: 30.5 knots	

The 1936 Royal Navy programme called for the construction of two 23,368-tonne (23,000-ton) carriers, and at first plans were drawn up based on *Ark Royal*. With the realization that war in Europe was coming ever closer, and that such carriers would be subject to constant air attack, armour protection and defensive armament was seen as important. The aircraft hangar was set in an armoured box intended to be proof against 227kg (500lb) bombs and 152mm (6in) guns.

Immediate action

Formidable was completed in Belfast in 1940. She deployed to the Mediterranean in March 1941 and was almost immediately in action, her aircraft achieving torpedo hits on the Italian battleship *Vittorio Veneto* and the cruiser *Pola* at the Battle of Cape Matapan. On 26 May 1941 she was badly damaged by German bombs off Crete. She underwent repairs in the USA and in 1943 was assigned to the Gibraltar-based Force H, her aircraft providing cover for the Allied landings in Sicily and Italy. In 1944 she was transferred to the Home Fleet, her aircraft taking part in attacks on the German battleship Tirpitz. In 1945 she joined the British Pacific Fleet and saw action off Okinawa, being twice damaged by kamikazes. On both occasions, her armoured flight deck saved her from serious harm.

HMS *Formidable* was placed in reserve in 1948, and went to the breaker's yard in 1953.

Howe

HMS *Howe* was the third of the King George V-class battleships. They adhered strictly to the limit of 35,000 tons imposed by the Naval Treaty, even though the treaty had expired before any of them was laid down.

COUNTRY: Great Britain
TYPE: Battleship
LAUNCH DATE: 1940
CREW: 1422
DISPLACEMENT: 36,725tons standard; 42,075tons full load
DIMENSIONS: 745ft x 103ft x 32ft 7in (227.05m x 31.4m x 9.95m)
RANGE: 15,000nm (27,800km) at 10 knots
ARMAMENT: 10 14in (356mm); 16 5.25in (135mm) AA; eight (later 22) 40mm; 32 (later 88) 2pdr pom-poms; up to 64 20mm; two aircraft
POWERPLANT: four-shaft, Parsons geared turbines; 110,000hp
PERFORMANCE: 28 knots

HMS *Howe* was one of the last and most powerful of the Royal Navy's battleships, her war service taking her from home waters to Japan.

Howe was built by Fairfield and commissioned in August 1942, by which time one of her sister ships, *Prince of Wales*, had already been sunk by Japanese aircraft. The upper strake of her protective belt ran for over half her total length, between the forward and after 14in (356mm) magazines, covering the machinery in between them.

Protection from torpedoes

Her torpedo protection system consisted of three vertical bands of compartments below the belt. The outer and inner were voids, the middle band being filled with fuel that was replaced with sea water as it was used. This was expected to be proof against a 1000lb (454kg) torpedo warhead; the four aerial torpedoes that sank the *Prince of Wales* were much smaller than this, but the two most important hits wrecked the propeller shafts. *Howe* was originally laid down as HMS *Beatty*, after the admiral who commanded the battlecruiser squadron at Jutland in 1916, but was renamed in 1940. She served with the Home Fleet and the Mediterranean until 1944, when sailed to join the British Pacific Fleet. She was placed on the reserve in 1951, and broken up at Inverkeithing in 1958.

HMS *Howe* was the flagship of the Royal Navy's Pacific Fleet in 1945, having taken part in the invasion of Sicily and Italy.

Hamakaze

Hamakaze was one of the Kagero class of Japanese destroyers. They embodied all the knowledge gained from the building and operation of previous classes.

COUNTRY: Japan
TYPE: Destroyer
LAUNCH DATE: 25 November 1940
CREW: 240
DISPLACEMENT: 2489 tonnes (2450 tons)
DIMENSIONS: 118.5m x 10.8m x 3.7m (388ft 9in x 35ft 5in x 12ft 4in)
RANGE: 8338km (4500nm)
MAIN ARMAMENT: Four 152mm (6in) guns; eight 610mm (24in) torpedo tubes
POWERPLANT: Two-shaft geared turbines
PERFORMANCE: 35.5 knots

Having fought her way through the Pacific war, _Hamakaze_ was sacrificed in what was virtually a suicide mission in April 1945.

Hamakaze and the other vessels of the Kagero class proved to be the ultimate in Japanese destroyer design, and were so successful that the subsequent class needed only minor modifications. *Hamakaze* was the first Japanese destroyer fitted with radar. On completion in 1941, she and her 17 sister ships were armed with six 152mm (6in) guns in twin turrets, but between 1943 and 1944, the turret on top of the aft superstructure was removed and replaced by additional anti-aircraft guns. The torpedo tubes were positioned amidships in enclosed quadruple mounts. Right from the beginning, she was part of the escort to the aircraft carrier task force that launched the air strike on Pearl Harbor. She was sunk on 7 April 1945, when large numbers of US carrier aircraft attacked a Japanese battle group, including the battleship *Yamato*, which was sailing to intercept American forces at Okinawa.

Only one surviving destroyer

The class saw extensive service during the Pacific war, six being lost in the bitter naval battles of 1943 that took place around the Solomon Islands. Of the 18 destroyers, in fact, only one - *Yukikaze* - survived the war, being surrendered at Maizuru. She was delivered to Nationalist China in 1947 as war reparation and renamed *Tan Yan*.

Hamakaze was involved in almost every Japanese naval operation in the Pacific during World War II.

Indomitable

The carrier *Indomitable* was to have been the fourth ship of the Illustrious class, but she ended up as a compromise, with lighter armour but more hangar space, allowing her to operate 50 per cent more aircraft.

Like other British carriers, *Indomitable* had a strongly armoured flight deck, which saved her from serious damage from kamikaze attacks.

COUNTRY: Great Britain
TYPE: Aircraft carrier
LAUNCH DATE: 1940
CREW:1329–2100
DISPLACEMENT: 23,000 tons standard; 29,730 tons full load
DIMENSIONS: 753ft 11in x 95ft 9in x 29ft (229.8m x 29.2m x 8.85m)
RANGE: 11,000nm (20,400km) at 14 knots
ARMAMENT: 16 4.5in (114mm); later 12 and later again 25 40mm; 24 (later 48) 2pdr pom-poms (later 36 20mm); 45 (later 56) aircraft
POWERPLANT: three-shaft, Parsons geared turbines; 111,000hp
PERFORMANCE: 30.5 knots

Indomitable, launched on 26 March 1940, was completed in October 1941. In November she went aground off Jamaica, delaying her deployment to the Indian Ocean, where she was to have provided the air component of the Eastern Fleet. In May 1942 she joined her sister ship *Illustrious* in attacking the Vichy French garrison on Madagascar, and in July 1943 she provided air cover for the Sicily invasion force. During these operations she was damaged by an Italian torpedo. In July 1944 she rejoined the Eastern Fleet, and with the carrier *Illustrious* began a series of attacks on enemy communications in Sumatra. In January 1945 she sailed from Trincomalee for Sydney, Australia, with the carriers *Illustrious*, *Indefatigable* and *Victorious* to form the nucleus of the British Pacific Fleet. In April, as part of Task Force 57, she saw action off Okinawa, where she was damaged in a kamikaze attack. She sustained more damaged in May, during attacks on the Sakishima Gunto island group.

Final mission

Her final mission of World War II was to lead the task force that reoccupied Hong Kong. She underwent a major refit after the war, was on the reserve list in 1953, and broken up two years later.

Indomitable was the fastest of the British fleet carriers, but some armour was sacrificed to increase her speed and aircraft complement.

Drum

Long-range ocean-going submarines like *Drum* were America's main means of striking back at the Japanese in the early months of 1942.

COUNTRY: USA
TYPE: Attack submarine
LAUNCH DATE: 12 May 1941
CREW: 80
DISPLACEMENT: Surfaced: 1854 tonnes (1825 tons), submerged: 2448 tonnes (2410 tons)
DIMENSIONS: 95m x 8.3m x 4.6m (311ft 9in x 27ft 3in x 15ft 3in)
SURFACE RANGE: 22,236km (12,000nm) at 10 knots
ARMAMENT: Ten 533mm (21in) torpedo tubes; one 76mm (3in) gun
POWERPLANT: Twin screw diesels, electric motors
PERFORMANCE: Surfaced: 20 knots, submerged: 10 knots

USS *Gato* was the lead ship in her class of submarine. She received 13 battle stars for service in World War II.

Drum was a double-hull, ocean-going submarine with good range. She was one of the Gato class of over 300 boats, and as such was part of the largest warship project undertaken by the US Navy. These boats, more than any others, were to wreak havoc on Japan's mercantile shipping in the Pacific war.

A devastating weapon

During her first offensive patrol in April 1942 *Drum* (Lt Cdr Rice) sank the seaplane carrier *Mizuho* and two merchant ships, and carried out vital reconnaissance work prior to the US landings in Guadalcanal. In October 1942 she sank three more ships off the east coast of Japan, and in December she torpedoed the Japanese carrier *Ryuho*. She sank a further two ships in April 1943, another in September, one in November, and three in October 1944, with another damaged. During this time there were no fewer than 54 American submarines operating in Japanese waters. The Japanese could only deploy one boat, the I-21, to distant waters, operating between Hawaii and the US west coast. US submarines applied a deadly stranglehold to Japan's remaining ocean lifelines, starving her of critical raw materials. *Drum* is now a museum exhibit.

The USS *Drum* operated in support of the American defence of Midway Island in 1942.

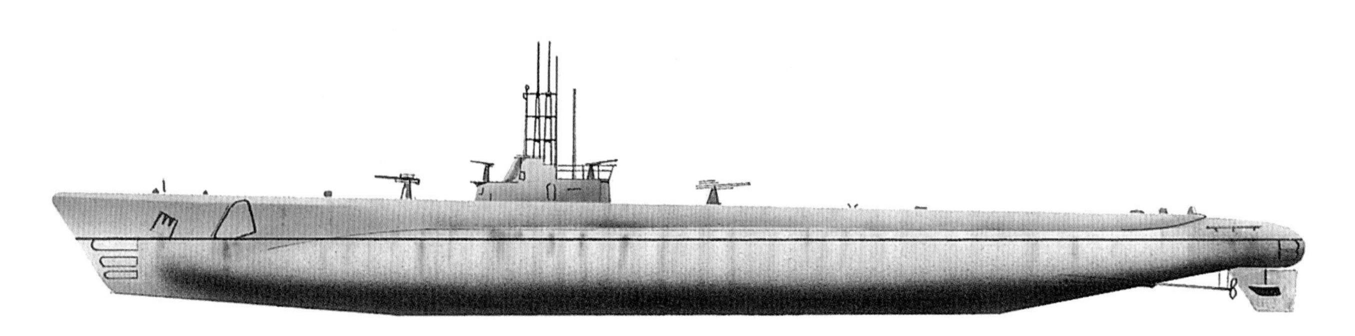

Essex

The Essex-class carriers were at the very core of the US Navy's Pacific campaigns from 1942 onwards, their aircraft protecting American invasion forces.

COUNTRY: USA
TYPE: Aircraft carrier
LAUNCH DATE: 31 July 1942
CREW: 2687
DISPLACEMENT: 35,438 tonnes (34,880 tons)
DIMENSIONS: 265.7m x 29.2m x 8.3m (871ft 9in x 96ft x 27ft 6in)
RANGE: 27,000km (15,000nm) at 12 knots
ARMAMENT: 12 127mm (5in) guns, 91 aircraft
POWERPLANT: Quadruple screw turbines
PERFORMANCE: 32.7 knots

The USS *Essex* is seen here with a formidable array of aircraft – she could accommodate 91 – on her flight deck.

By the end of the 1930s, the increased needs of the navy for air cover led to an explosion in the size of aircraft carriers, and a larger hull was introduced to stow the aviation fuel required for the 91 aircraft now carried.

A highly effective raider

There were 24 vessels in the Essex class, their designs based around an enlargement of the earlier Yorktown–class carriers. *Essex* was laid down in April 1941 and entered service in 1942. She was removed from the effective list in 1969 and scrapped in 1973. *Essex*'s battle honours in World War II included raids on Marcus and Wake Islands, the Gilbert Islands and Kwajalein (1943); raids on Truk and the Marianas, Saipan, Guam, Tinian, Palau and the Battle of the Philippine Sea (1944); raids on Luzon, the China coast, the Ryukus, Iwo Jima, Okinawa and Japan (1945). In November 1944 the carrier was damaged by a kamikaze hit at Leyte, and again in April 1945 off Okinawa. *Essex* was decommissioned in January 1947, but from 1949 to 1951 she underwent a major refit, hydraulic catapults being added. Recommissioned in January 1951, she sailed for Korean waters. In September 1951 she was damaged by an aircraft crash-landing on her flight deck. In 1955–6 she underwent further construction, being fitted with an angled flight deck, after which she served with the US Atlantic and Pacific Fleets. She was refitted in 1962, but was decommissioned seven years later. She was sold and broken up in 1975.

Six unnamed carriers of the Essex class were cancelled at the end of World War II. The others continued to serve for many years.

Fletcher

A highly successful design, the Fletcher–class destroyers formed the backbone of the US Pacific Fleet from 1942 until the end of the Pacific war.

The Fletcher-class destroyers were designed specifically for operations in the Pacific, where range was of paramount importance.

The Benson-class design had limitations for a Pacific war, both in terms of endurance and its weapons. Even before the end of the programme, therefore, the first of an improved class were coming off the slipways. The first two of this Fletcher class went down the ways in February 1942 and the last four of 175 ships on the same day in September 1944 at Puget Sound Navy Yard. Fletcher class vessels were generally rushed out to the Pacific on completion, but those built on the Atlantic seaboard saw some service there. USS *Fletcher* served on convoy protection duty in the western Atlantic before sailing to the Pacific in time for the naval actions off Guadalcanal. She was reclassified as a destroyer escort (DDE) in 1949. One of the best-known destroyers in this class was the USS *Johnston*.

The Fletcher-class destroyers were designed primarily as escort vessels, a role they performed with admirable efficiency.

Battle of Leyte

During the Battle of Leyte in October 1944 she was one of seven destroyers assigned to Rear-Admiral Sprague's Task Unit 3. On 24 October, Sprague's force intercepted a force of Japanese warships attempting to escape to Leye Gulf through the San Bernadino Strait. Torpedoes from the *Johnston* and another destroyer, the *Hoel*, hit the Japanese cruiser *Kujmano* and stopped her dead in the water, but the two UD destroyers came under heavy fire from the battleships *Yamato* and *Nagato* and both were sunk.

COUNTRY: USA

TYPE: Destroyer

LAUNCH DATE: 3 May 1942

CREW: 295

DISPLACEMENT: 2083 tonnes (2050 tons)

DIMENSIONS: 114.76m x 12.04m x 5.41m (376ft 6in) x 39ft 6in x 17ft 9in)

RANGE: 7412km (4000nm)

MAIN ARMAMENT: Five single 127mm (5in) D; three twin 40mm (1.5in) AA and four single 20mm(0.7in) AA guns; two quintuple 533mm (21in) torpedo tubes

POWERPLANT: Two sets of geared steam turbines, two shafts

PERFORMANCE: 37 knots

Iowa

The Iowa-class battleships were the largest and fastest of their kind ever constructed for the US Navy. They were also the last.

COUNTRY: USA
TYPE: Battleship
LAUNCH DATE: 27 August 1942
CREW: 1921
DISPLACEMENT: 56, 601 tonnes (55, 710 tons)
DIMENSIONS: 270.4m x 33.5m x 11.6m (887ft 2in x 108ft 3in x 38ft)
RANGE: 27,000km (15,000nm) at 12 knots
ARMAMENT: nine 406mm (16in), 20 127mm (5in) guns
POWERPLANT: Quadruple screw turbines
PERFORMANCE: 32.5 knots

Freed of treaty-imposed restrictions, the *Iowa*'s designers were able to attempt to create the best possible battleship, and the fact that all the ships of her class were still in operational service half a century after she was completed shows they succeeded. The designers' only 'artificial' constraint was that the ships must have a beam of no more than 33.55m (110ft) in order to pass through the Panama Canal. Their impressive performance was obtained by giving them 60 per cent more power than the preceding class of South Dakotas, and increasing their length by almost 30 per cent. The long, narrow bow, with its considerable sheer, was an unmistakeable *Iowa* feature.

In 2007 there were plans to turn *Iowa* into a floating museum in California.

The USS *Iowa* turning under speed. The number 61 on her bow identifies her.

Participant in all major Pacific battles

The USS *Iowa* was commissioned on 22 February 1943 and operated in the Atlantic for almost a year before deploying to the Pacific. She saw action in all the major battles of the Pacific war in 1944–5, being damaged by shore batteries off Mili Island in March 1944, and continued to serve with the Pacific Fleet until 1948, when she was decommissioned. She was recommissioned in 1951 for bombardment duty off Korea, then served with the Atlantic Fleet until 1958, when she was again decommissioned. Back in service in 1984, she escorted merchant vessels in the Persian Gulf during the Iraq-Iran war. In 1989 an explosion in one of her gun turrets killed 47 officers and men. She was paid off in 1990 and laid up.

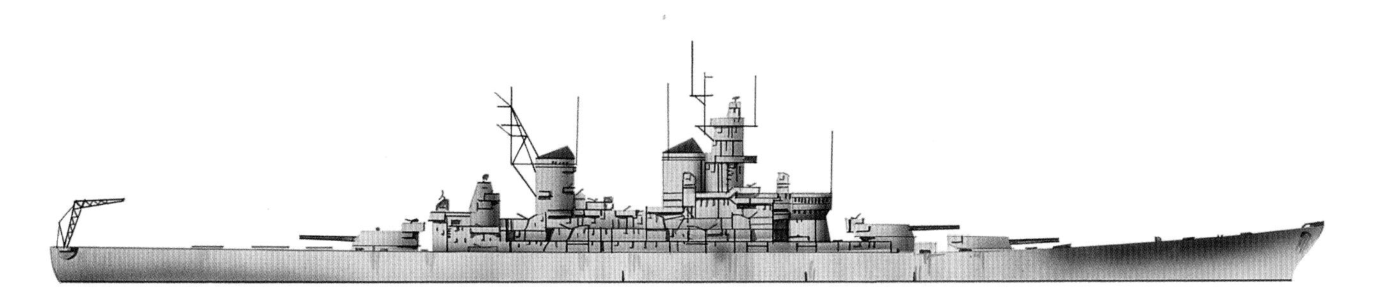

Canberra

The Baltimore-class cruisers remained in service after World War II, some serving as flagships and support vessels in Vietnam. Five, including *Canberra*, became guided missile cruisers.

The Baltimore-class standard heavy cruisers shared a common ancestry with, and were similar in appearance to, the slightly earlier Cleveland class. Both began as improved versions of the heavy cruiser variant of the Brooklyn class. However, the design of the Baltimores included improvements to the hull that eliminated the topweight problems that had affected the smaller Clevelands. Most of the extra tonnage went into improving hull strength, rather than improvements in armour protection. Originally commissioned in 1941 as a Baltimore-class cruiser, *Canberra* saw much war service in the central Pacific from 1944, in the battle for Truk and in heavy raids on Japanese-held islands as part of the US Task Group 58.

COUNTRY:	USA
TYPE:	Cruiser
LAUNCH DATE:	19 April 1943
CREW:	1544
DISPLACEMENT:	18,234 tonnes (17,947 tons)
DIMENSIONS:	205.4m x 21.25m x 7.6m (673ft 5in x 69ft 8in x 24ft 11in)
RANGE:	13,140km (7300nm) at 12 knots
ARMAMENT:	Two Terrier surface-to-air missiles (72 missiles per launcher), six 203mm (8in), 10 127mm (5in) guns
POWERPLANT:	Four shaft geared turbines
PERFORMANCE:	33 knots

One of the main ways to recognize *Canberra* was by her sharply angled bow.

Rebuilt as a missile cruiser

In October 1944, she was badly damaged by a torpedo off Okinawa. She was rebuilt and recommissioned in 1955 as one of two Boston-class missile cruisers. *Canberra* and her sister *Boston* were the first US Navy vessels designed as anti-aircraft missile ships and were rushed into service during the Cold War. They were armed with Terrier missiles in place of their aft turrets. In addition, other ships were converted to increase the US Navy's anti-aircraft missile capability. *Canberra* was stricken in 1978.

***Canberra* and her sister *Boston* were the first of several generations of warships that were to become key elements of a surface fleet.**

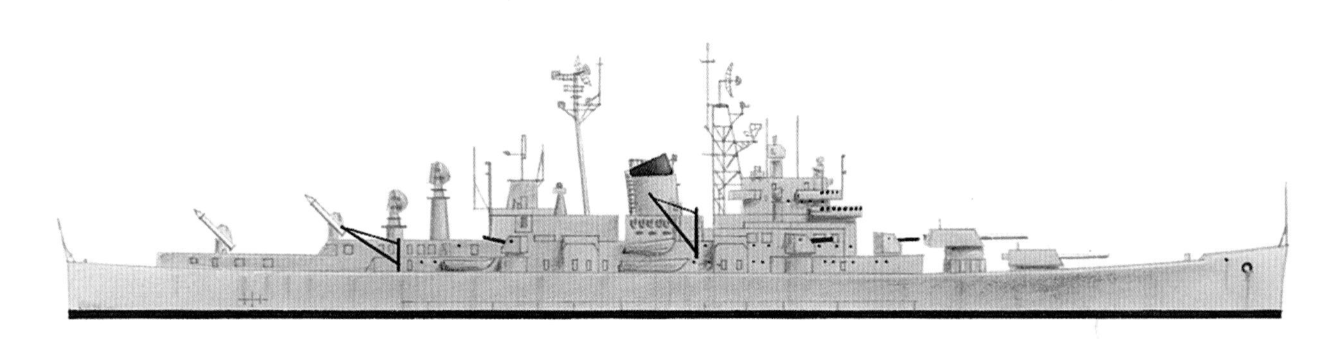

Gambier Bay

Although they were based on the hulls of merchant vessels, the Casablanca-class escort carriers, to which *Gambier Bay* belonged, were the first of their kind to be purpose-built, and not converted merchantmen.

COUNTRY: USA
TYPE: Aircraft carrier
LAUNCH DATE: 22 November 1943
CREW: 860
DISPLACEMENT: 11,074 tonnes (10,900 tons)
DIMENSIONS: 156.1m x 32.9m x 6.3m (512ft 3in x 108ft x 20ft 9in)
RANGE: 18,360km (10,200nm) at 12 knots
ARMAMENT: One 127mm (5in), 16 40mm (1.6in) guns, 27 aircraft
POWERPLANT: Twin screw, reciprocating engines
PERFORMANCE: 19 knots

Ships like the *Gambier Bay* proved indispensable to the US Navy's war effort, especially in the Pacific.

In mid-1942 the industrial magnate Henry J. Kaiser, whose concerns were already engaged in the mass production of merchant vessels, came up with a proposal to build 100 light escort carriers within a year, using the same construction methods. The result was the Casablanca class, work on which proceeded rapidly with the full approval of President Roosevelt, who saw the urgent need for more aircraft carriers in all theatres of war. The class was designed to carry an air group of nine fighters, nine bombers and nine torpedo-bombers. The first mission for *Gambier Bay* was in early 1944, when she ferried aircraft to USS *Enterprise* and then supported US forces off Saipan, in the Marianas, and later at Leyte. She was sunk by gunfire during action off Samar in October 1944.

Epic sea-fight

Her loss occurred during one of the most epic sea-fights of the war, when the lightly armed escort carrier groups supporting the invasion of the Philippines fought off the main Japanese battle fleet in a surface action. The survivors of the class were all laid up at the end of the war.

The *Gambier Bay* and her 49 sister ships were simple, functional vessels.

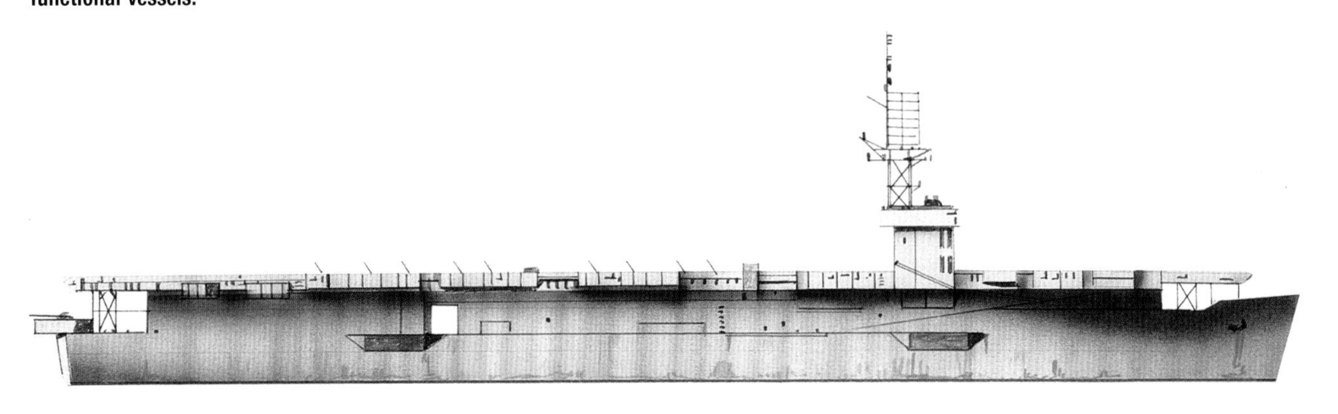

I-400

The submarines of the I-400 class were designed to combine the scouting and attack duties of all earlier types. The original design also provided a facility to carry two bomber aircraft.

COUNTRY: Japan
TYPE: Attack submarine
LAUNCH DATE: 1944
CREW: 100
DISPLACEMENT: Surfaced: 5316 tonnes (5233 tons), submerged: 6665 tonnes (6560 tons)
DIMENSIONS: 122m x 12m x 7m (400ft 1in x 39ft 4in x 24ft)
SURFACE RANGE: 68,561km (37,000nm) at 14 knots
ARMAMENT: Eight 533mm (21in) torpedo tubes; one 140mm (5.5in) gun
POWERPLANT: Twin screws, diesel/electric motors
PERFORMANCE: Surfaced: 18.7 knots, submerged: 6.5 knots

The Japanese realized too late that success in the Pacific lay in the production of very large ocean-going submarines such as the I-400.

Prior to World War II, several navies tried to build an effective aircraft-carrying submarine. Only the Japanese managed to produce a series of workable vessels. Of the 19 planned vessels only two, the I-400 and I-401, were completed for their intended role. A third, I-402, was completed as a submersible tanker transport. I-400 was a huge vessel, with a large aircraft hangar offset to starboard, to hold three M6A1 Seiran floatplanes, plus components for a fourth. To launch the aircraft, I-400 would surface, then the machines would be warmed up in the hangar, rolled out, wings unfolded, and launched down a 26m (85ft) catapult rail. It was planned to attack the locks on the Panama Canal, but the mission was never flown.

The I-400 could remain at sea for 90 days and had a huge radius of action. At the end of the war I-400 and I-401 surrendered at sea to US Naval forces, I-400 surrendering to the destroyer USS *Blue*.

Handed over to the US Navy

They were then sent to Yokosuka where they were handed over to the US Navy, who carried out trials with them and then sailed them to the USA, where they were sunk as target vessels in 1946. The third boat, I-402, was surrendered at Kure and taken to Sasebo, where she was sunk by the US Navy. The I-400 class was not rivalled in size until the emergence of the Ethan Allen class.

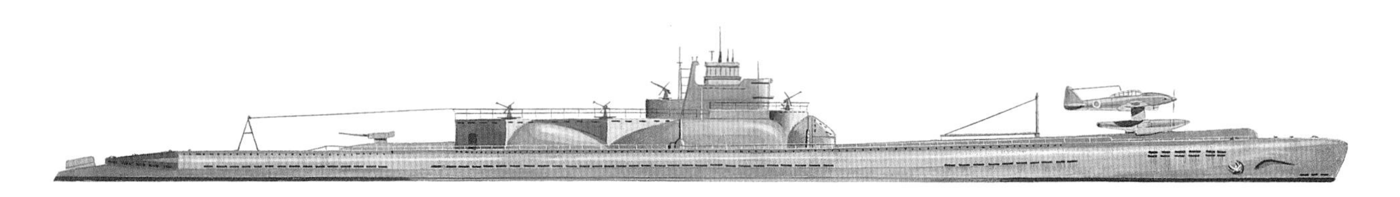

The I-400–class boats were an ambitious undertaking, built at the express wish of Admiral Yamamoto.

Eagle

HMS *Eagle* was one of Britain's first post-war aircraft carriers, and gave excellent service in the 'limited wars' and police actions in which the Royal Navy became involved.

COUNTRY: Great Britain
TYPE: Aircraft carrier
LAUNCH DATE: 19 March 1946
CREW: 2740
DISPLACEMENT: 47,200 tonnes (46,452 tons)
DIMENSIONS: 245m x 34m x 11m (803ft 9in x 112ft 9in x 36ft)
RANGE: 7412km (4000nm) at 20 knots
ARMAMENT: 16 112mm (4.5in) guns
POWERPLANT: Quadruple screw turbines
PERFORMANCE: 32 knots

HMS *Eagle* rendered exceptional service to the Royal Navy during the most dangerous year of the Cold War.

With the completion of the 1936 and 1937 naval construction programmes and with the construction of the Illustrious-class carriers of 1938 in progress, designs were prepared in 1942 for their successors. These allowed for two complete hangars with the capacity to hold the heavier aircraft that were anticipated. HMS *Eagle* was originally laid down at the Harland and Wolff shipyard as the *Audacious*, being renamed *Eagle* in January 1946.

Striking the Suez Canal zone

She was launched on 19 March that year. *Eagle* and *Ark Royal* were improvements on the Implacable type, with a greatly enlarged armoured hangar enabling them to carry 81 aircraft, nearly twice as many as their predecessors and bringing them more into line with their US counterparts. *Eagle* entered service in October 1951, decommissioned in January 1972, and sent for breaking up in 1978. She was the sister ship of HMS *Ark Royal*. During her service career she took part in many peacekeeping actions, but she is perhaps best remembered for her offensive role in the Anglo-French Suez operations, when her aircraft carried out numerous strikes on targets in the Suez Canal zone in support of Anglo–French ground forces.

Eagle was reconstructed in 1959–64, being provided with an angled flight deck, steam catapult and missile armament.

Daring

The Daring-class destroyers of the early 1950s were unusual. They were manned as light cruisers, with a captain in charge instead of a commander and a crew subjected to a routine that included bugle calls instead of pipes.

The Daring-class destroyers of the Royal Navy became a familiar sight on the oceans of the world during the Cold War era.

Launched in 1949, *Daring* and her seven sisters were expanded and improved versions of the earlier Battle-class and Weapon-class vessels, and were able to perform a variety of tasks, including anti-submarine and reconnaissance duties. They were the largest destroyers built for the Royal Navy and had an all-welded hull construction. The 120mm (4.5in) guns were radar-controlled and automatic. The lattice foremast was built around the fore funnel, giving *Daring* an unusual and distinctive appearance. During the early years of the Cold War, the vessels of the Daring class formed an important part of NATO's hunter-killer naval forces in the Atlantic. They were the first British destroyers specifically designed to perform multi-role functions, and set the trend for future developmetns that would lead to today's highly effective craft.

A new and powerful breed

To follow the Daring class, the British Admiralty proposed a new and more powerful breed known as the '1953 destroyer' – vessels with sufficiently high speed and firepower to close with and engage the Soviet Navy's new Sverdlov-class cruisers. The ships were to be armed with a large 5in gun that would fire a folding-fin, discarding-sabot shell at 96 rounds per minute (later scaled down to 8l0rpm). The design was dropped in 1955.

COUNTRY: Great Britain

TYPE: Destroyer

LAUNCH DATE: 25 November 1949

CREW: 98

DISPLACEMENT: 264 tonnes (260 tons)

DIMENSIONS: 56.6m x 5.7m (185ft 6in x 19ft)

RANGE: Not known

MAIN ARMAMENT: One 12-pounder; three six-pounders; three torpedo tubes

POWERPLANT: Twin screw three-stage compound engines

PERFORMANCE: 22 knots

Daring **was a very purposeful vessel, well fitted to serve the Royal Navy's interests within NATO and elsewhere.**

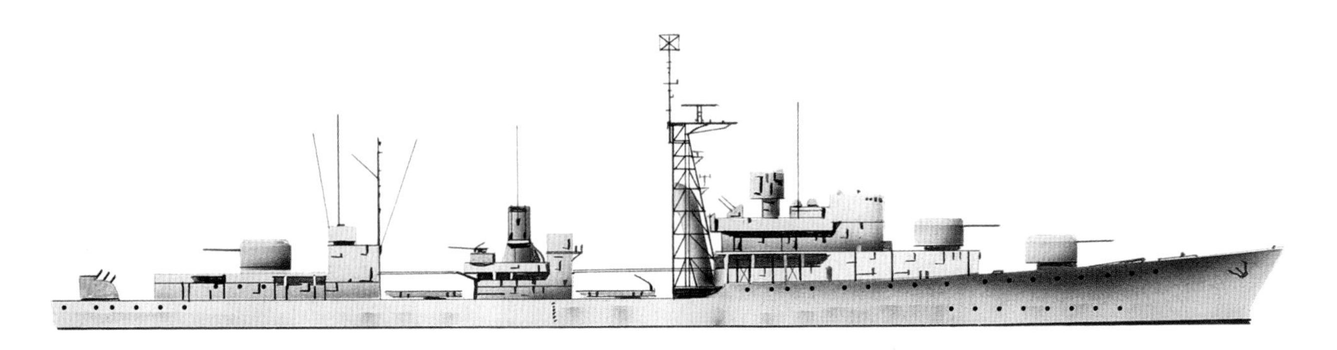

Hermes

Because of her role in the Falklands War, HMS *Hermes* became one of the best-known aircraft carriers ever to have served in the Royal Navy. Her active service career was continued as the INS *Vikrant* in the Indian Navy.

COUNTRY: Great Britain	
TYPE: Aircraft carrier	
LAUNCH DATE: 16 February 1953	
CREW: 1830 and 270 air group	
DISPLACEMENT: 25,290 tonnes (24,892 tons)	
DIMENSIONS: 224.6m x 30.4m x 8.2m (737ft x 100ft x 27ft)	
RANGE: 7412km (4000nm) at 15 knots	
ARMAMENT: 32 40mm (1.6in) guns	
POWERPLANT: Twin screw turbines	
PERFORMANCE: 29.5 knots	

HMS *Hermes* was a much-travelled ship, having been deployed to every area of the world during her lengthy career.

In 1943 designs were drawn up for a class of eight carriers, with machinery installed that was twice as powerful as that in the earlier Colossus class. Armour was to be improved, and a stronger flight deck was planned to handle the heavier aircraft then entering service. Eventually, only four ships were laid down, and the Admiralty decided to scrap these while they were still on the stocks at the end of World War II. Due to the inability of many existing carriers to handle the new jet aircraft, construction was continued. Two of the ships in this class, *Albion* and *Bulwark*, were built with a partly angled flight deck and steam catapults, *Centaur* being similarly modified in 1957.

Further modifications

Hermes, first named HMS *Elephant*, was built with further modifications; she was reconstructed in 1964-6 with a fully angled flight deck and steam catapult. *Albion* and *Bulwark* were converted to the role of Commando Carrier, exchanging their fixed-wing aircraft for helicopters.

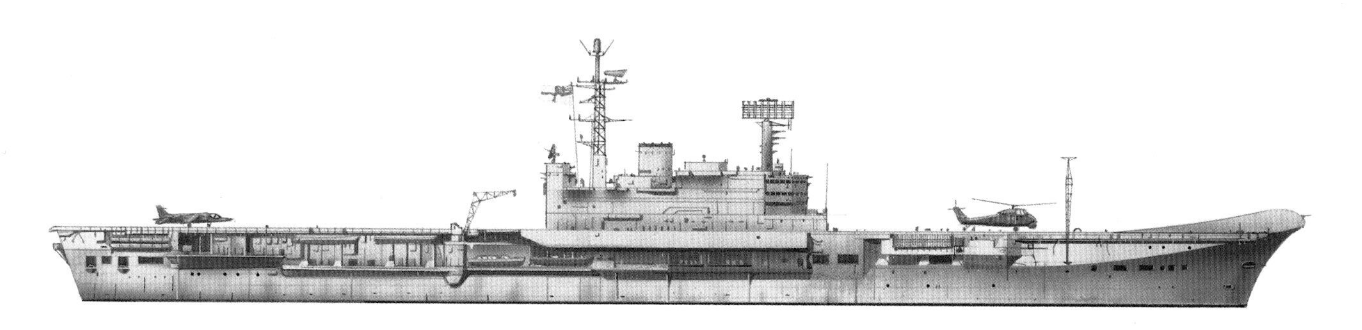

HMS *Hermes* pictured after being fitted with a 'ski ramp' to enable her to operate the British Aerospace Sea Harrier.

Forrestal

Originally designed as attack carriers, the Forrestal class later adopted a multi-mission role, anti-submarine aircraft being added to their air groups

The USS *Forrestal* was a huge vessel for her day, as is clearly shown in this photograph.

COUNTRY: USA
TYPE: Aircraft carrier
LAUNCH DATE: 11 December 1954
CREW: 2764 crew, 1912 air crew
DISPLACEMENT: 80,516 tonnes (79,248 tons)
DIMENSIONS: 309.4m x 73.2m x 11.3m (1,015ft x 240ft x 37ft)
RANGE: 21,600km (12,000nm) at 10 knots
ARMAMENT: Eight 127mm (5in) guns, 90 aircraft
POWERPLANT: Quadruple screw turbines
PERFORMANCE: 33 knots

Forrestal and her three sisters of the Forrestal class were authorized in 1951. Their large size was needed to operate fast combat jets, which required more fuel than their piston-engined predecessors. Designed with an angled flight deck and four steam catapults, *Forrestal* had space for around 3.4 million litres (750,000 gallons) of aviation fuel and 1670 tonnes (1650 tons) of aviation ordnance.

Operations off Vietnam

She served with the Atlantic Fleet until 1965, when she underwent a refit before being transferred to the Pacific Fleet for operations off Vietnam. On 29 July, 1967, *Forrestal* was en route to 'Yankee Station' off Vietnam, with aircraft armed and fuelled on deck. As an auxiliary power unit was backed into position to start up an F-4 Phantom, its hot exhaust blew directly on to a Zuni rocket pod and ignited one of the rockets, which streaked across the busy flight deck and hit a loaded F-4, which burst into flames. The fire quickly spread below decks, touching off bombs and ammunition. Above deck, the blaze was extinguished in an hour, but below decks it raged for a full 12 hours. Acts of extreme bravery that day involved bombs and rockets from burning aircraft being thrown overboard: 134 personnel died and 62 were injured. *Forrestal* was refitted in 1983-5 and then stricken and placed in storage in 1993.

The USS *Forrestal* was named after James Vincent Forrestal (1892–1949), America's first Secretary of Defense.

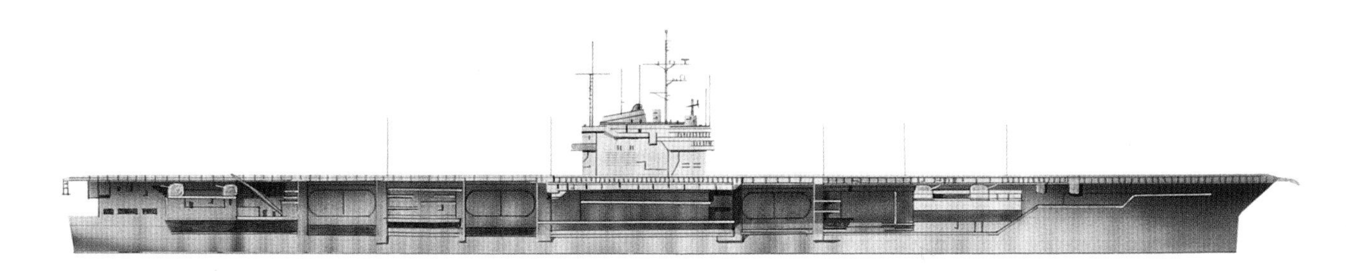

Nautilus

On 3 August 1958 the USS *Nautilus* became the first submarine to reach the North Pole, cruising under the Arctic icecap. Her commander recorded the event with the historic signal, 'Nautilus ninety degrees north.'

COUNTRY: USA

TYPE: Attack submarine

LAUNCH DATE: 21 January 1954

CREW: 105

DISPLACEMENT: Surfaced: 4157 tonnes (4091 tons), submerged: 4104 tonnes (4040 tons)

DIMENSIONS: 97m x 8.4m x 6.6m (323ft 7in x 27ft 8in x 21ft 9in)

RANGE: Unlimited

ARMAMENT: Six 533mm (21in) torpedo tubes

POWERPLANT: Twin screws, one S2W reactor, turbines

PERFORMANCE: Surfaced: 20 knots, submerged: 23 knots

With the launching of the nuclear-powered USS *Nautilus*, the world of submarines would never be the same again.

Work on a nuclear reactor plant for submarines began in 1948. Development was in the hands of a group of scientists and engineers at the Naval Reactors Branch of the Atomic Energy Commission, led by Captain Hyman G. Rickover, USN. The penalty for failure would have been immense; not only was there a huge amount of money involved, but the prestige of the USA was at stake.

No fear of failure

Rickover and his team never doubted they would succeed, and in December 1951 the Department of the Navy was confident enough to order a hull for the nuclear plant. *Nautilus* was the world's first nuclear-powered submarine. Apart from her revolutionary propulsion system, she was conventional. Early trials set new records, including nearly 2250km (1213nm) submerged in 90 hours at 20 knots, the longest period spent underwater by a US submarine, as well as being the fastest speed submerged. There were two prototype nuclear attack submarines; the other, USS *Seawolf*, was launched in July 1955, the last US submarine to have a conning tower, as distinct from the fin of later nuclear submarines. *Nautilus* was the more successful; *Seawolf* had S2G reactor, intended as a backup to the S2W, but it had many operational problems and was replaced by an S2W in 1959. *Nautilus* was preserved as a museum exhibit at Groton, Connecticut, in 1982.

The USS *Nautilus* was launched on 21 January 1954 by First Lady Mrs Eisenhower, and commissioned eight months later.

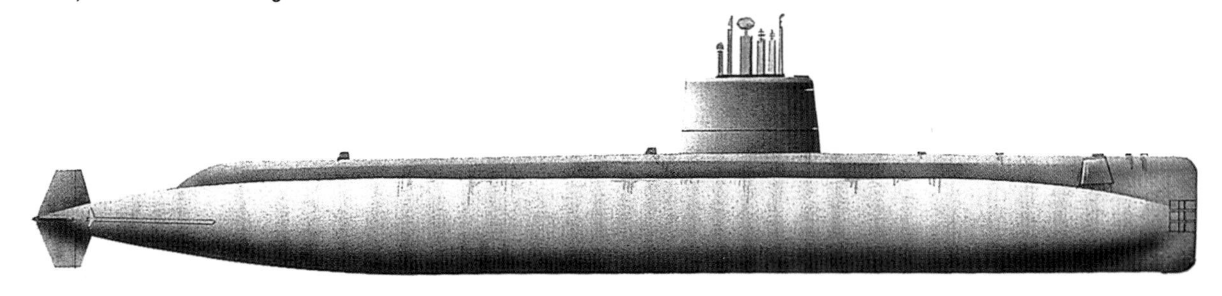

Clémenceau

The *Clémenceau* and her sister ship *Foch* were the first aircraft carriers designed and built from the keel to be completed in France. The French Navy's first carrier, the *Arromanches*, was the former HMS *Colossus*.

COUNTRY: France
TYPE: Aircraft carrier
LAUNCH DATE: 21 December 1957
CREW: 1338, or 984 (as a helicopter carrier)
DISPLACEMENT: 33,304 tonnes (32,780 tons)
DIMENSIONS: 257m x 46m x 9m (843ft 2in x 150ft x 28ft 3in)
RANGE: 13,500km (7500nm) at 12 knots
ARMAMENT: Eight 100mm (3.9in) guns, 40 aircraft
POWERPLANT: Twin screw geared turbines
PERFORMANCE: 32 knots

The *Clémenceau*'s air group comprised a mixture of Dassault Étendard strike jets and Breguet Alizé anti-submarine aircraft.

Despite suffering from a succession of rapidly changing governments and policies, the French Navy recovered extremely well from the years of the German occupation and in building up a world-class military potential. New aircraft carriers were a key element of the navy's reconstruction plans and they were partly funded by the US Mutual Assistance Pact, as France was at that time still part of NATO. *Clémenceau* (R98) and her sister *Foch* (R99) were originally intended as part of class of six fleet carriers, but only two were built. *Clémenceau* was ordered from Brest dockyard in May 1954, while *Foch* began construction at St Nazaire and was completed at Brest.

Gulf War participant

These were the first French purpose-built carriers, and *Clémenceau* underwent constant modification during design and construction. She served the French Navy well, operating in the Pacific, off the coast of Lebanon, and taking part in the 1991 Gulf War. During her career she was extensively modernized, with new defensive weapons and command systems added. Her air wing normally comprised 16 Super Étendards, 3 Étendard IVP, 10 F-8 Crusaders, 7 Alizé, plus helicopters. In later years she operated more helicopters than fixed-wing aircraft. She was replaced by the nuclear-powered *Charles de Gaulle*.

***Clémenceau* underwent a substantial refit in 1957–8, an angled flight deck and other improvements being added.**

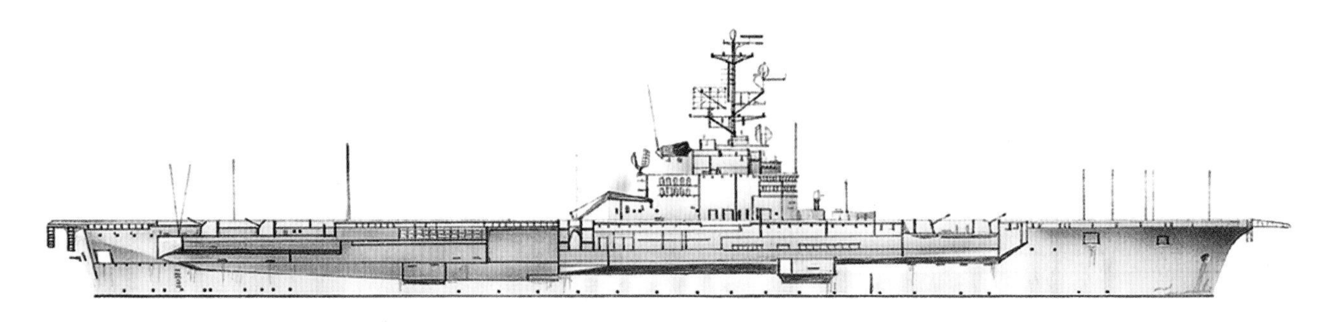

Foxtrot

The *Foxtrot* was the most successful of the Soviet Union post-war conventional submarine designs, and was frequently encountered on patrol by NATO forces during the Cold War.

The Foxtrot class diesel-electric submarines were the best, and most popular, of their type to see service with the Soviet Navy.

COUNTRY: Soviet Union	
TYPE: Attack submarine	
LAUNCH DATE: 1959 (first unit)	
CREW: 80	
DISPLACEMENT: Surfaced: 1950 tonnes (981 tons), submerged: 2500 tonnes (2540 tons)	
DIMENSIONS: 91.5m x 8m x 6.1m (300ft 2in x 26ft 3in x 20ft)	
SURFACE RANGE: 10,190km (5500nm) at 8 knots	
ARMAMENT: Ten 533mm (21in) torpedo tubes	
POWERPLANT: Three shafts, three diesel engines and three electric motors	
PERFORMANCE: Surfaced: 18 knots, submerged: 16 knots	

The 1960s witnessed a marked development in Soviet maritime activities involving new construction and an increasingly bold fleet policy. Previously, in accordance with Soviet military doctrine, the Navy had been little more than an extension of the Red Army, with naval strategy based on homeland defence.

Naval exercises in the North Sea

The sight of Soviet warships on the high seas was extremely rare. This began to change in July 1961, when the first large Soviet out-of-area exercise took place, with eight surface combatant units, associated support vessels and four submarines exercising in the Norwegian Sea. The submarines were the new 'Foxtrot' class. Built in the periods 1958–8 (45 units) and 1971–4 (17 units), the Foxtrot-class diesel-electric submarine remained in production at a slow rate for export, the last unit being launched in 1984. The class was the most successful of the post-war Russian conventional submarine designs, 62 serving with the Soviet Navy. Three Soviet Navy Fleet Areas operated 'Foxtrot', and the Mediterranean and Indian Ocean Squadrons regularly had these boats deployed to them. India, the first foreign recipient received eight between 1968 and 1976, followed by Libya, with six units received between 1976 and 1983, and Cuba, three boats being handed over between 1979 and 1984. All Soviet Foxtrots were withdrawn by the late 1980s.

'Foxtrot' was the NATO reporting name for the submarine designated Project 641 by the Russians. It replaced the earlier Zulu class.

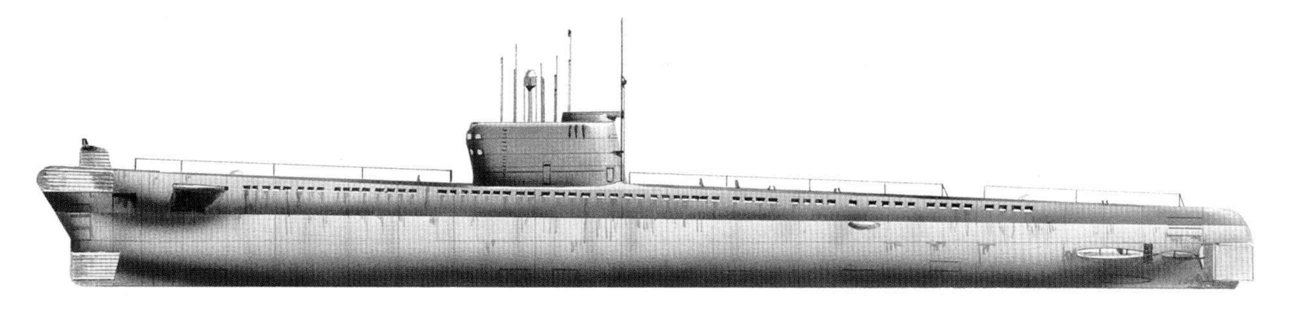

George Washington

The *George Washington* was the first vessel in the Western world to be armed with ballistic missiles. When she entered service, a new type of capital ship was born: the Strategic Warfare Ship.

COUNTRY: USA
TYPE: Ballistic missile submarine
LAUNCH DATE: June 1959
CREW: 112
DISPLACEMENT: Surfaced: 6115 tonnes (6019 tons), submerged: 6998 tonnes (6888 tons)
DIMENSIONS: 116.3m x 10m x 8.8m (381ft 7in x 33ft x 28ft 10in)
RANGE: Unlimited
ARMAMENT: Sixteen Polaris missiles, six 533mm (21in) torpedo tubes
POWERPLANT: Single screw, one pressurized water-cooled reactor, turbines
PERFORMANCE: Surfaced: 20 knots, submerged: 30.5 knots

Like all nuclear submarines, the *George Washington* was capable of travelling at speed both submerged and underwater.

In 1955, the Soviet Union began modifying six existing diesel submarines to carry nuclear-tipped ballistic missiles. America was simultaneously developing the Jupiter missile, which was to equip a projected 10,160-tonne (10,000-ton) nuclear submarine. Jupiter used a mix of highly volatile propellant liquids, and was posing huge safety and operation problems. The smaller, lighter Polaris A1 presented a more suitable alternative. The nuclear submarine *Scorpion*, then building, was chosen as the delivery platform for the new weapon and a new 40m (13ft) hull section was added just aft of the conning tower to house 16 missiles in vertical launch tubes.

The other submarines in the George Washington class were *Patrick Henry, Theodore Roosevelt, Robert E. Lee* and *Abraham Lincoln.*

Winning the nuclear arms race

Renamed *George Washington*, she was the first of a new type of weapons platform, and put the US far ahead in the nuclear arms race. The *George Washington* successfully fired two Polaris A1 missiles while submerged off Cape Canaveral in the first underwater launching of a ballistic missile from a US submarine. All five submarines of this class were refitted to fire the improved Polaris A3 missile, and equipped with the Mk 84 fire control systems and gas-steam (as distinct from compressed air) missile ejectors.

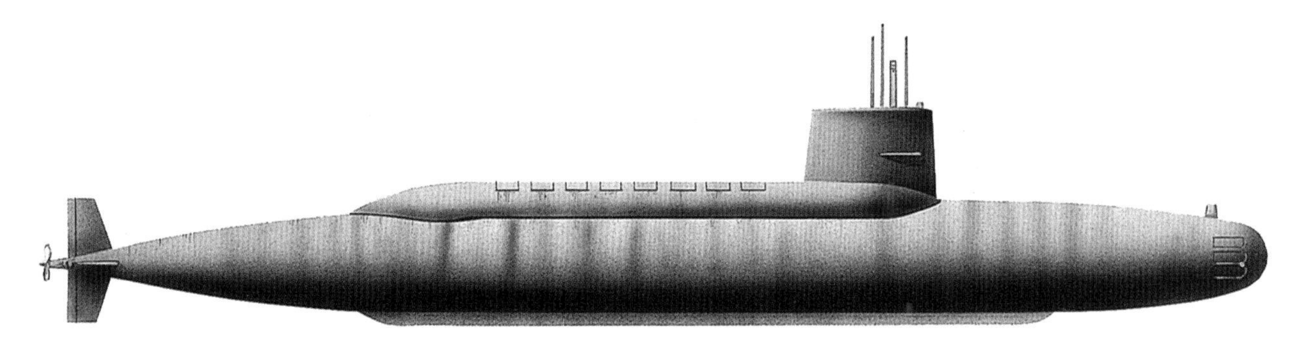

Boykiy

The Krupny-class destroyers, of which *Boykiy* was one, were improved Kotlins armed with SS-N-1 anti-ship missiles. They were the first Soviet warships to have a helicopter platform as standard.

In the early 1960s four Kotlin-class destroyers were modified on the stocks to carry the SS-N-1 surface-to-surface ballistic missile. The Kidlin class, as these were known, were the world's first guided-missile destroyers. Following this successful experiment, the eight Krupny class (intended as gun-armed successors to the Kotlins) were also fitted with SS-N-1 SSMs. They were the first Soviet class to have a helicopter platform, the helicopter probably being necessary to provide a mid-course correction link with the missiles. Initial construction started in 1958 at Leningrad. Original armament was the SS-N-1 anti-ship missile, but when this became obsolete the whole group was converted to the anti-submarine warfare role.

COUNTRY: Soviet Union
TYPE: Destroyer
LAUNCH DATE: 15 December 1960
CREW: 360
DISPLACEMENT: 4826 tonnes (4750 tons)
DIMENSIONS: 140m x 15m x 5m (458ft 9in x 45ft 9in x 16ft 6in)
RANGE: 11,112km (6000nm)
Main ARMAMENT: Eight 57mm (2.25in) guns, plus missiles
POWERPLANT: Twin screw geared steam turbines
PERFORMANCE: 34 knots

The Krupny-class destroyers ushered the Soviet Navy into the missile age, and were important units of the Soviet fleet.

Helicopter fitted as standard

Other ships in the class were the *Gnevnyi*, *Gordyi*, *Plamyonny* and *Zorkyi*. They were the first Soviet destroyers to have a helicopter platform fitted as standard, probably because a helicopter was needed to provide mid-course corrections to the anti-ship missiles. They were also the last developments of the original Kotlin destroyer concept to be built, later designs making use of gas turbine propulsion or new high-pressure steam plant. Three ships of the class were converted to the SAM role.

The helicopter landing pad is clearly visible in this illustration of *Boykiy*.

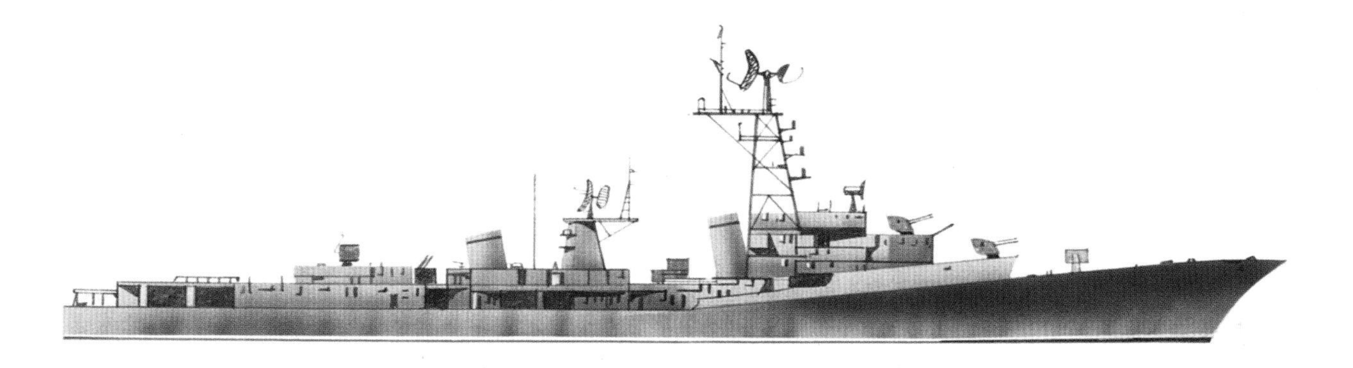

Dreadnought

Launched on Trafalgar Day, 21 October 1960, HMS *Dreadnought* was the Royal Navy's first nuclear-powered attack submarine (SSN), and was specifically designed to hunt and destroy hostile undersea vessels.

COUNTRY: Great Britain

TYPE: Attack submarine

LAUNCH DATE: 21 October 1960

CREW: 88

DISPLACEMENT: Surfaced: 3556 tonnes (3500 tons), submerged: 4064 tonnes (4000 tons)

DIMENSIONS: 81m x 9.8m x 8m (265ft 9in x 32ft 3in x 26ft 3in)

RANGE: Unlimited

ARMAMENT: Six 533mm (21in) torpedo tubes

POWERPLANT: Single screw, nuclear reactor, steam turbines

PERFORMANCE: Surfaced: 20 knots, submerged: 30 knots

HMS *Dreadnought*, like her battleship predecessor of over half a century earlier, was a revolutionary step forward for the Royal Navy.

She was powered by an American S5W reactor, which was also used in the US Navy's Skipjack-class nuclear submarines; subsequent Royal Navy SSNs had a British-designed nuclear plant. *Dreadnought* began sea trials in 1962. The Royal Navy carried out much pioneering work with *Dreadnought*, including proving the concept of using nuclear submarines to act as escorts for a fast carrier task group; the results of this work were made available to the US Navy, which had a close relationship with the Royal Navy at this time. Although used as a trials vessel, *Dreadnought* was a fully–capable SSN.

Improved crew accommodation

Accommodation for the *Dreadnought*'s crew was of a standard that had been impossible to attain in any previous British submarine. For the first time, an improved water distilling plant provided unlimited fresh water for shower baths and for washing machines in a fully equipped laundry. Separate mess spaces were provided for senior and junior ratings, on either side of a large galley where food was served on a cafeteria system. Particular attention was paid to the decoration and furnishing of living quarters and to recreational facilities, which included a cinema.

***Dreadnought*'s primary role was as a submarine hunter-killer, for which she was equipped with the latest underwater detection gear.**

Foch

Construction of France's Clémenceau-class aircraft carrier *Foch* was undertaken at the Chantiers de l'Atlantique at St Nazaire in a special dry dock. She was towed to Brest for completion.

COUNTRY: France
TYPE: Aircraft carrier
LAUNCH DATE: 28 July 1960
CREW: 1338 (as aircraft carrier), 984 (as helicopter carrier)
DISPLACEMENT: 32,255 tonnes (32, 780 tons)
DIMENSIONS: 265m x 31.7m x 8.6m (870ft x 104ft x 28ft)
RANGE: 13,500km (7500nm) at 12 knots
ARMAMENT: Eight 100mm (3.9in) guns, Crotale and Sadral surface-to-air missile systems, 40 aircraft
POWERPLANT: Two shaft, geared steam turbines
PERFORMANCE: 32 knots

A smart vessel, the aircraft carrier *Foch* was a manifestation of France's determination to be a leading naval power.

Laid down in 1957 and completed in 1963, *Foch* is the second of the Clémenceau class carriers. Both *Clémenceau* and *Foch* were were first intended to be built as light fleet carriers, with an armament of twenty-four 2.25in guns in twin mountings, but the armament was revised to twelve 100mm (3.9in) guns in 1956 and to eight weapons of similar calibre in 1958, the guns having a rate of fire of 60 rounds per minute. *Foch* was completed with anti-torpedo bulges, *Clémenceau* being similarly modified during one of her refits. She underwent a refit between 1981 and 1982 which enabled her to carry tactical nuclear weapons, and in 1984 received a satellite communications system. Further improvements included a point-defence missile system in place of 100mm (3.9in) guns, a new catapult mechanism and a laser landing system.

Forced to share an air group

Her missile system was improved again in 1996, yet *Foch* failed to retain a full air group. From 1975 on she shared one with her sister *Clémenceau* and was used as a helicopter carrier. Her strike component consisted of the Super Étendard attack aircraft, armed with AN52 15kT nuclear bombs. She was sold to the Brazilian Navy in 2001 as the *São Paulo*.

The selling of surplus aircraft carriers to 'Third World' navies became common practice for the French and British arms industries.

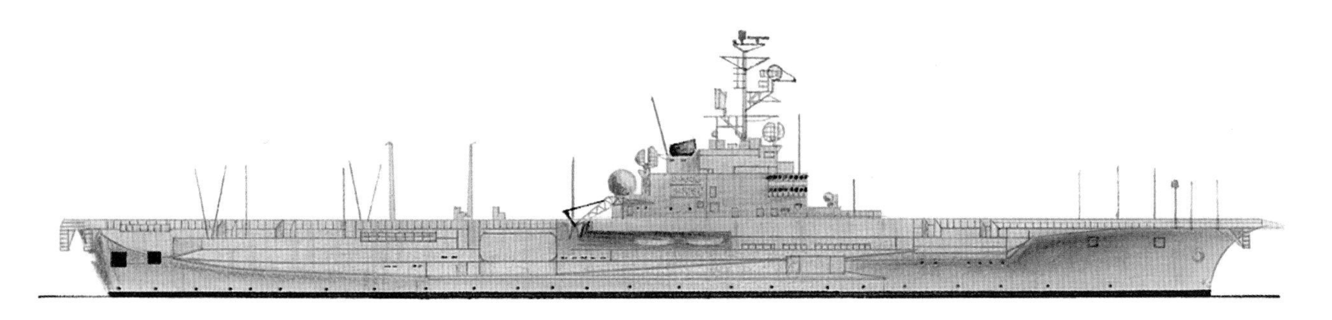

Gurkha

The Tribal class frigates were designed for the specialist roles of preceding classes, while remaining capable of meeting the main escort functions of anti-submarine warfare, anti-aircraft defence and aircraft direction.

COUNTRY: Great Britain
TYPE: Frigate
LAUNCH DATE: 11 July 1960
CREW: 253
DISPLACEMENT: 2743 tonnes (2700 tons)
DIMENSIONS: 109m x 12.8m x 5.3m (360ft x 42ft x 17ft 6in)
RANGE: 7778km (4200nm)
MAIN ARMAMENT: Two 114mm (4.5in) guns; one Limbo three-barrelled anti-submarine mortar
POWERPLANT: Single screw, turbine and gas turbine
PERFORMANCE: 28 knots

HMS *Gurkha* was to have been the leader of a much larger class of general-purpose frigate, but an air-defence version was cancelled.

Launched in 1960, *Gurkha* was one of seven general-purpose frigates in the Tribal class. They among the first ships to be fully air-conditioned in all crew areas and most working spaces. The standard steam turbine developed 12,500hp, and this could be boosted by a gas turbine to increase output to 20,000hp. Highly seaworthy, the ships made good speed even in unfavourable sea states.

Carrying anti-submarine helicopters

Of the ships in this class, *Ashanti*, *Eskimo* and *Gurkha* were ordered under the 1955–6 British Navy Estimates, *Nubian* and *Tartar* under the 1956–7 programme, and *Mohawk* and *Zulu* under 1957–8. The ships, of welded prefabricated construction, were all completed between 1961 and 1964. They were the first frigates designed to carry a helicopter for anti-submarine reconnaissance. *Gurkha* was sold to Indonesia in 1984. At one point it was proposed to introduce a specialized air-defence version of the Tribal class armed with Tartar surface-to-air missiles. The planned eight vessels were cancelled in 1963, but the design was used as the basis for a class of four Canadian anti-submarine destroyers, *Iroquois*, *Huron*, *Athabaskan* and *Algonquin*. These had the same hull designs, dimensions and basic characteristics as the Tribals, but with greatly enhanced anti-submarine warfare features.

***Gurkha* and the other 'Tribals' were designed with economy in mind, combining several specialist roles in one hull.**

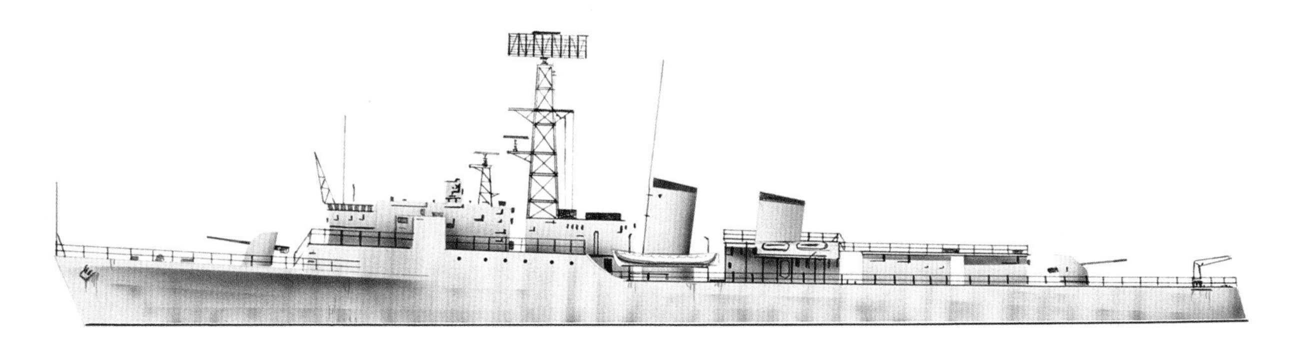

Iwo Jima

The Iwo Jima-class amphibious assault ship was the world's first ship class built specifically to operate helicopters. Each could carry a Marine battalion landing team and a reinforced helicopter squadron.

In a world where rapid deployment to trouble spots was essential, vessels such as *Iwo Jima* assumed a new degree of importance.

COUNTRY: USA

TYPE: Helicopter carrier

LAUNCH DATE: 17 September 1960

CREW: 667, plus 2000 troops

DISPLACEMENT: 18,330 tonnes (18,042 tons)

DIMENSIONS: 183.6m x 25.7m x 8m (602ft 8in x 84ft x 26ft)

RANGE: 11,118km (6000nm) at 18 knots

ARMAMENT: Four 76mm (3in) guns

POWERPLANT: Single screw turbines

PERFORMANCE: 23.5 knots

Ever since 1955, when the former escort carrier *Thetis Bay* was converted to the role of helicopter assault ship, the US Navy has maintained a vertical airlift capability for the US Marine Corps. The Iwo Jima-0class ships were built to an improved World War II escort carrier design. They were the first in any navy to be designed specifically to carry and operate helicopters, and as such no catapult or arrester gear was fitted. *Iwo Jima* can also carry a Marine battalion of 2000 troops, plus their artillery and support vehicles.

Extensive onboard medical facilities

The flight deck allows for the simultaneous take-off of up to seven helicopters, and *Iwo Jima* has hangar facilities for up to 20 helicopters. Storage capacity is provided for 1430 litres (6500 gallons) of petrol for the vehicles, plus over 88,000 litres (400,000 gallons) for the helicopter force. In 1970 a Sea Sparrow missile launcher was installed, followed by a second three years later. *Iwo Jima* and her six sisters have extensive medical facilities, including operating theatres as well as a large hospital. Other vessels in the class are *Guadalcanal*, *Guam*, *Inchon*, *Okinawa*, *Tripoli* and *New Orleans*.

***Iwo Jima* takes her name from one of the bloodiest and grimmest Marine operations of the Pacific war.**

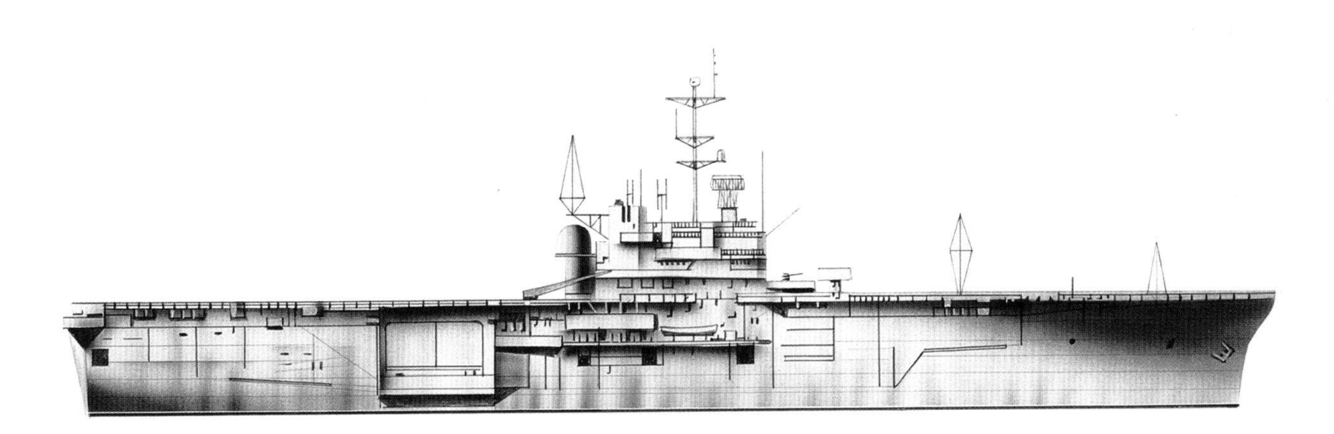

Kashin

The Kashin class destroyers first entered service in the early 1960s with the last of 20 units commissioning in 1972. Some underwent extensive modifications to form the 'Kashin Mod' sub-class.

COUNTRY: Soviet Union
TYPE: Destroyer
LAUNCH DATE: 31 December 1960 (Komsomolets Ukrainy, first unit)
CREW: 280
DISPLACEMENT: 4572 tonnes (4500 tons)
DIMENSIONS: 144m x 15.8m x 4.8m (472ft 5in x 51ft 10in x 15ft 9in)
RANGE: 15,750km (8504nm)
MAIN ARMAMENT: Two twin 76mm (3in) guns; 4 533mm (21in) torpedo tubes; SA-N-1 SAMs; ASW rockets
POWERPLANT: Two shafts, four gas turbines
PERFORMANCE: 36 knots

The Kashin-class destroyers formed an important part of Soviet fleet deployments during the 1960s.

Built as the world's first major class of warships to be powered by gas turbines, the Kashin class was built from 1959 onwards at the Zhdanov shipyard in Leningrad (five units 1962–6) and at the 61 Kommuna (North) shipyard at Nikolaiev (15 units 1959–72).

Disaster at sea

In 1972, one of the Nikolaiev-built ships, *Otvzhny*, foundered in the Black Sea following an explosion and fire that raged out of control for five hours until the destroyer sank. Over 200 of her crew lost their lives, making this the worst peacetime naval disaster since the end of World War II. The last of the class, *Sderzhanny*, was completed to a revised design designated *Kashin II*, and three further units were built in the late 1970s for the Indian Navy, named *Rajput*, *Rana* and *Ranjit*. The Kashin class was prolific in all the Soviet Navy's operational areas and first came to the attention of NATO in 1963, during the Soviet Navy's bi–annual exercises. In March and April seven surface units plus support ships exercised near the Lofotens, and in August a similar force conducted exercises in the Iceland-Faeroes Gap. Part of this group circumnavigated the British Isles before returning to the Baltic. The exercises held the next year saw the introduction of the latest missile-armed warships.

Although construction of the Kashin class for the Soviet Navy ceased in 1972, it was introduced in modified form for export to India.

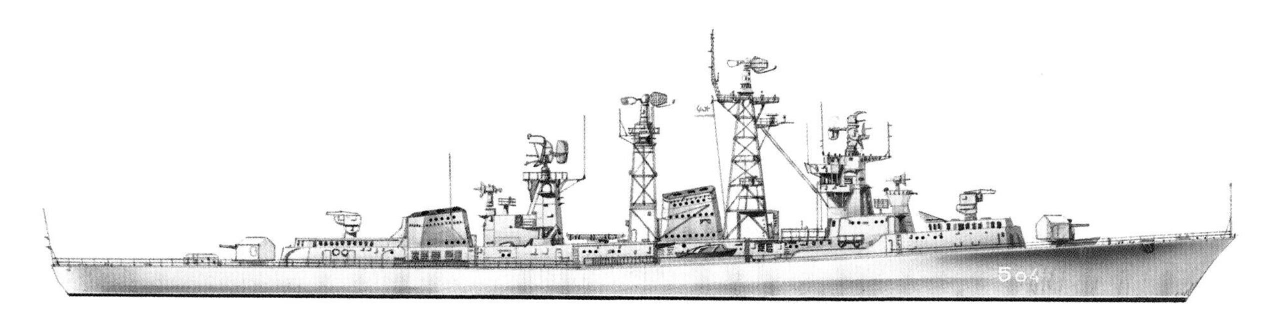

Dido

The Leander-class frigates were built in several batches, the Batch 3 variants being the most powerful. HMS *Dido* was a Batch 1 vessel.

COUNTRY: Great Britain	
TYPE: Frigate	
LAUNCH DATE: 22 December 1961	
CREW: 263	
DISPLACEMENT: 2844 tonnes (2800 tons)	
DIMENSIONS: 113.3m x 12.4m x 5.4m (372ft x 41ft x 18ft)	
RANGE: 8334km (4500nm)	
MAIN ARMAMENT: Two 114mm (4.5in) guns; one quadruple launcher for Seacat SAMs	
POWERPLANT: Twin screw turbines	
PERFORMANCE: 30 knots	

A Leander-class frigate with a 'bone in her teeth' ploughs at speed through the Atlantic.

Over the centuries, the frigate has performed tasks, ranging from the classic 'eyes of the fleet' of Nelson's day to the suppression of the U-boat menace in the Battle of the Atlantic. During the Cold War era the frigate became the 'workhorse' of NATO's navies, the term being applied to vessels ranging from very expensive and highly specialized anti-submarine warfare vessels to cheaper anti-aircraft ships designed to escort convoys and groups of amphibious warships.

Royal Navy frigate backbone

The 26-strong Leander class became the backbone of the Royal Navy's frigate force during the 1960s and early 1970s. Vessels of this class followed the basic pattern of the Rothesay/Whitby class, but were more versatile and had improved fighting capabilities. *Dido*, launched in December 1961, had an early-warning radar, bow-mounted sonar, and variable-depth sonar. Along with her guns and missiles, she had a triple-barrelled anti-submarine mortar. She also carried a Wasp light helicopter (later replaced by a Lynx) equipped with anti-submarine homing torpedoes. Some ships in this class, *Dido* included, had their guns replaced by the Ikara anti-submarine missile system. Several nations bought Leanders, or built them under licence. *Dido* was sold to New Zealand in 1983 as the *Southland*, and has now been stricken.

These frigates had a distinctive silhouette, with a stepped-up bow forward of the gun turret and a large radar array aft of the funnel.

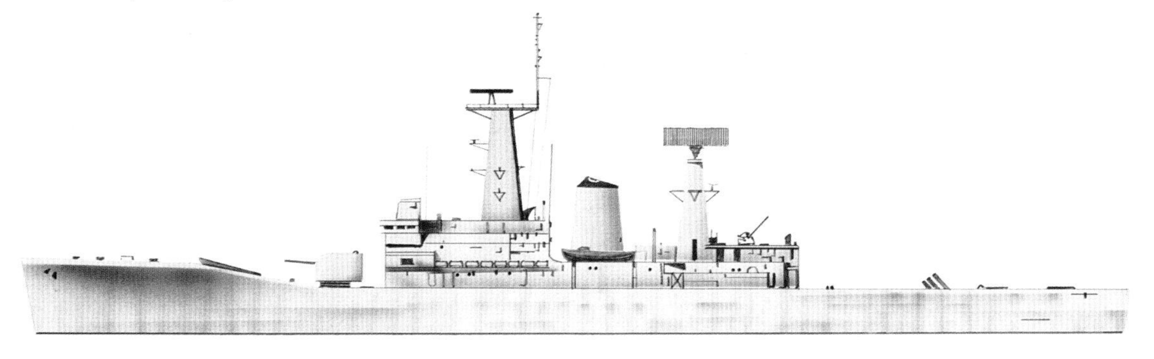

Daniel Boone

Larger than most cruisers of World War II, ballistic missile submarines like the *Daniel Boone* are without parallel in their awesome destructive power.

COUNTRY: USA
TYPE: Ballistic missile submarine
LAUNCH DATE: 22 June 1963
CREW: 140
DISPLACEMENT: Surfaced: 7366 tonnes (7250 tons), submerged: 8382 tonnes (8250 tons)
DIMENSIONS: 130m x 10m x 10m (425ft x 33ft x 33ft)
RANGE: Unlimited
ARMAMENT: Sixteen Polaris missiles, four 533mm (21in) torpedo tubes
POWERPLANT: One water-cooled nuclear reactor, turbines
PERFORMANCE: Surfaced: 20 knots, submerged: 35 knots

Viewed from any angle, an American SSBN is an awesome sight on the surface.

During the Cold War, the nuclear-powered ballistic missile submarine (SSBN) and the submarine-launched ballistic missile were the sword and shield of the Eastern and Western power blocs. With vast areas of the world's oceans to roam on long submerged patrols, the boats provide an almost totally immune second strike capability against the opposing bloc's population centres and industrial base.

Upgrading warheads

When the *Daniel Boone* was launched, no one could have foreseen that the most likely target would be a 'rogue' state. Although actually two classes, the 12 Benjamin Franklin-class and the 19 Lafayette-class of nuclear-powered ballistic-missile submarines (SSBN) were similar in appearance, but the former were built with quieter machinery outfits. The *Daniel Boone* (SSBN629) was one of the Lafayette class. As built, the first eight Lafayettes carried the 16 Polaris A2 submarine-launched ballistic missiles (SLBMs), each with a single 800kT yield warhead, but the rest were armed with the Polaris A3; this replaced by the Poseidon C3. Between September 1978 and December 1982 12 units were converted to carry the Trident I C4 SLBM. The boats were progressively deactivated as the Trident-armed Ohio-class SSBNs entered service.

Pictured is an AV-8B of VMAT 203, the USMC Harrier Training Squadron, NAS Cherry Point, North Carolina.

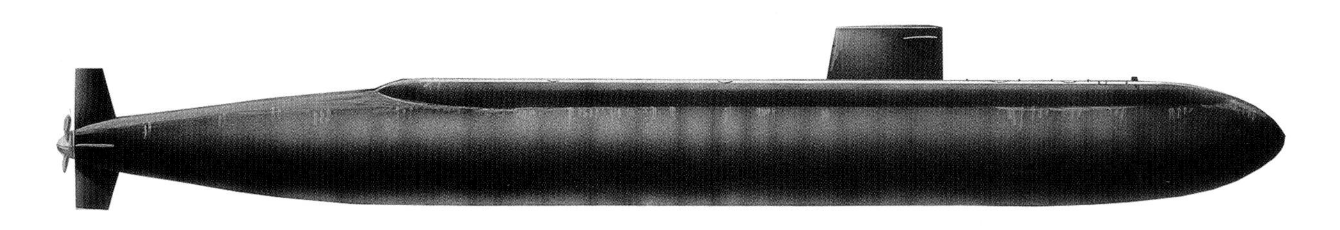

Galatea

Ships of the Leander class were initially armed with the Short Seacat surface-to-air missile. The Wasp, and later Lynx, helicopters carried by the class each carried two homing torpedoes.

The 'mattress-type' air warning radar antenna at the top of the mainmast was a main recognition feature of the Leander class.

COUNTRY: Great Britain
TYPE: Frigate
LAUNCH DATE: 23 May 1963
CREW: 263
DISPLACEMENT: 2906 tonnes (2860 tons)
DIMENSIONS: 113.4m x 12.5m x 4.5m (372ft x 41ft x 14ft 9in)
RANGE: 8519km (4600nm)
MAIN ARMAMENT: One anti-submarine Ikara missile launcher
POWERPLANT: Twin screws, turbines
PERFORMANCE: 28 knots

One of the Leander class designed in the late 1950s, planned as improved versions of the Type 12 Rothesay class, and intended to be built in five batches spread over 10 years, *Galatea* was part of the first group of seven vessels. In all, 24 were to be built, the later ships increasing in size and carrying more equipment, including Exocet and updated electronics. The hull had a long, unbroken form, with a raised forecastle. The hangar for one or two ASW helicopters was situated aft. The Ikara ASW missile system in *Galatea* was housed forward on the extended superstructure in front of the bridge. The initial design of the all-weather *Ikara* was undertaken by the Australian government, but when the Royal Navy expressed an interest in the system the programme became a joint one with British Aerospace. *Ikara* was powered by a solid-fuel combined booster and sustainer rocket, and in all its configurations it was launched on a bearing that would bring it to a torpedo-release position close to the target.

A highly successful class

Data for the latter's position was supplied either by the launch platform's own sonar or by a remote data-linked source. The class was updated during the 1970s and 1980s, and progressively withdrawn from 1988 onwards. The success of the class was measured by the fact that it sold overseas, and was built under licence in some countries.

Leander-class frigates like *Galatea* served the Royal Navy well, and enjoyed considerable export success.

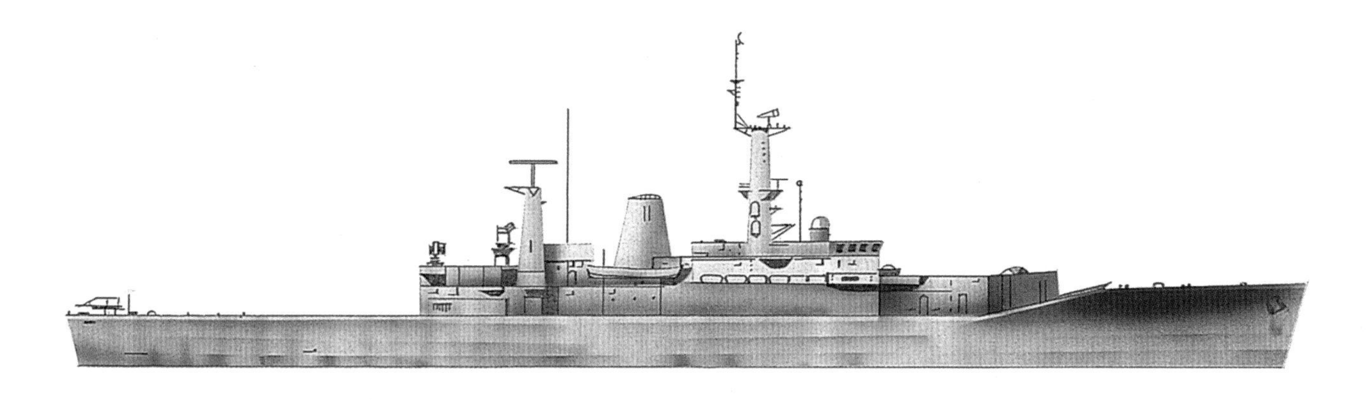

Moskva

The *Moskva* was essentially a stop-gap vessel. Her design did not lend itself to good handling at sea, and she was soon relegated to the reserve with the appearance of the more effective Kiev class carriers.

Country:	Soviet Union
Type:	Helicopter carrier
Launch date:	14 January 1965
Crew:	850
Displacement:	14,800 tonnes (14,567 tons)
Dimensions:	191m x 34m x 7.6m (626ft 8in x 111ft 6in x 25ft)
Range:	8100km (4500nm) at 12 knots
Armament:	One twin SUW-N-1 launcher, two twin SA-N-3 missile launchers, 14–20 helicopters
Powerplant:	Twin screw turbines
Performance:	30 knots

The helicopter carrier *Moskva* seen during fleet manoeuvres in the Mediterranean shortly after she became operational.

Moskva was the first helicopter carrier built for the Soviet Navy. Laid down in 1962 and completed in 1967, she was designed to counteract the growing threat from the US nuclear-powered missile submarines that first entered service in 1960, and to undertake search and destroy missions.

Building programme terminated

Moskva had a massive central block that housed the major weapons systems, and a huge sonar array. However, by the time *Moskva* and *Leningrad* had been built at the Nikolayev South shipyard, they were incapable of coping with both the numbers and capabilities of NATO submarines, so the building programme was terminated.

Moskva and her sister ship, _Leningrad_, had a cumbersome, top-heavy appearance and were not good sea boats in heavy weather.

Classed by the Russians as PKR (Protivolodochnyy Kreyser, or anti-submarine cruiser) the ships proved to be poor sea boats in heavy weather.

After spending some time with the Soviet 5th Eskadra in the Mediterranean, *Moskva* and her complement of helicopters sailed to join the Northern Fleet and put in an appearance in an exercise that at first seemed to follow the traditional 'defence of the homeland' theme. However, in a departure from former practice in the Norwegian Sea, the Soviet forces conducted anti-submarine warfare operations in the area northeast of Jan Mayen Island. *Leningrad* was stricken in 1991, *Moskva* in 1996. Both were scrapped.

Carabiniere

The Italian frigates *Alpino* and *Carabiniere* were smart vessels, and were equipped to carry two Agusta-Bell ASW helicopters. They were fitted with land, air and surface surveillance radar.

COUNTRY: Italy
TYPE: Frigate
LAUNCH DATE: 30 September 1967
CREW: 254
DISPLACEMENT: 2743 tonnes (2700 tons)
DIMENSIONS: 113m x 13m x 4m (371ft x 43ft 6in x 12ft 7in)
RANGE: 7408km (4000nm)
MAIN ARMAMENT: Six 76mm guns; six 305mm (12in) torpedo tubes; one A/S mortar
POWERPLANT: Twin screw, diesels, gas turbines
PERFORMANCE: 28 knots (all engines)

***Alpino* pictured with one of her Agusta-Bell ASW helicopters on the helipad astern.**

The Italian frigates *Alpino* and *Carabiniere*, originally named *Circe* and *Climene*, were provided for under the 1959–60 programme. The original Circe-class project was modified in 1962. The new design was an improved version of the Centauro class, combined with the Bergamini class. They had similar basic characteristics, but a heavier displacement and increased engine power. Two other ships of the same type, to have been named *Perseo* and *Polluce*, were provided for under the 1960–1 programme, but were suspended for reasons of economy. The Alpino-class frigates were the first Italian warships to be powered by gas turbines, but they were capable of making a steady 22 knots on diesels alone. Part of their task was to provide an ASW screen for the US Sixth Fleet, based on Naples, Sigonella and La Maddalena in Italy, with its headquarters at Gaeta near Naples. During the Cold War it provided the unity and strength which were otherwise lacking in Mediterranean NATO, especially after Britain relinquished her bases on the island of Malta.

Sharing narrow waters

Anti-submarine warfare protection of the kind provided by the Italian frigates was crucial in an area where the US were compelled to share the narrow waters with the Soviet Mediterranean Squadron and its very dangerous submarines. *Alpino* is now a mine-countermeasures ship and *Carabiniere* is a weapons-trial vessel.

After relinquishing her duties as an escort vessel, *Carabiniere* adopted another important role, testing new naval weapons systems.

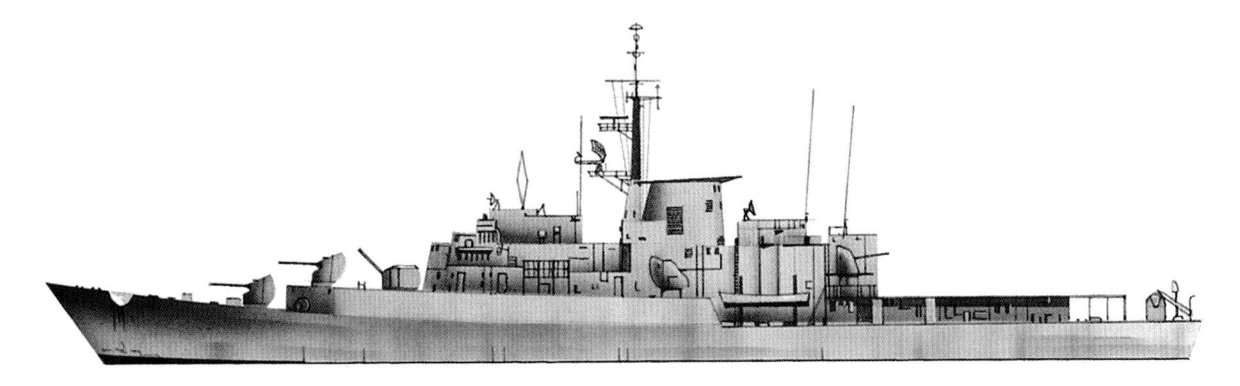

Charlie class

The Charlie I class were the first Soviet nuclear-powered guided-missile submarines capable of launching surface-to-surface cruise missiles without having to surface first.

The Charlie I class SSGN carried the SS-N-7 J-band active radar homing anti-ship missile in two banks of four missile tubes.

COUNTRY: Soviet Union	
TYPE: Attack submarine	
LAUNCH DATE: 1967	
CREW: 100	
DISPLACEMENT: Surfaced: 4064 tonnes (4000 tons), submerged: 4877 tonnes (4800tons)	
DIMENSIONS: 94m x 10m x 7.6m (308ft x 32ft 9in x 25ft)	
RANGE: Unlimited	
ARMAMENT: Eight SS-N-7 cruise missiles, six 533mm (21in) torpedo tubes	
POWERPLANT: Nuclear, one pressurized water reactor, one steam turbine	
PERFORMANCE: Surfaced: 20 knots, submerged: 27 knots	

Charlie class were similar to the Victor class, visible differences including a bulge at the bow, the vertical drop of the forward end of the fin, and slightly lower after casing. The Charlie I carried the SS-N-15 nuclear-tipped anti-submarine missile(range of 37km [20nm]) and the SS-N-7 submerged-launch anti-ship missile.

Return to base to reload

The Charlie Is were all built at Gorky between 1967 and 1972. One was leased to India in January 1988, and another sank off Petropavlovsk in June 1983; it was later salvaged, only to sink again by its jetty agai 1985. The last 10 were decommissioned in the 1990s. The Charlie II class, built from 1972–80 at Gorky, was an improved Charlie I with a 9m (29ft 6in) insertion in the hull forward of the fin to house the electronics and launch systems necessary for targeting and firing the SS-N-15 and SS-N-16 weapons. In both Charlie classes, once the missiles were expended the submarine returned to base to be reloaded. The six Charlie II boats were also armed with the SSN-9 Siren anti-ship missile, which cruises at 0.9 Mach and has a range of 110km (60nm) and can be fitted with either a nuclear (250kT) or conventional warhead. The Charlie II-class vessels were all based with the Northern Fleet, and made occasional deployments to the Mediterranean before decommissioning in the mid-1990s.

The hull of the Charlie-class submarines had considerable depth, as this illustration shows.

Conqueror

For nearly 30 years, NATO and Warsaw Pact submariners played a deadly game of cat and mouse in the world's oceans, the tools of their trade being nuclear attack submarines (SSNs). One such was HMS *Conqueror*.

COUNTRY: Great Britain	
TYPE: Attack submarine	
LAUNCH DATE: 28 August 1969	
CREW: 116	
DISPLACEMENT: Surfaced: 4470 tonnes (4400 tons), submerged: 4979 tonnes (4900 tons)	
DIMENSIONS: 86.9m x 10.1m x 8.2m (285ft x 33ft 3in x 27ft)	
RANGE: Unlimited	
ARMAMENT: Six 533mm (21in) torpedo tubes	
POWERPLANT: Nuclear, one pressurized water reactor	
PERFORMANCE: Surfaced: 20 knots, submerged: 29 knots	

HMS *Conqueror*, seen here in peaceful surroundings, sank the *General Belgrano* with two unguided Mk 8 torpedoes.

The main advantages of the nuclear attack submarine are its ability to remain submerged for virtually unlimited periods, its deep-diving capability, its long-range sensor systems, and the high power of its reactor. The later generations of attack submarines are truly underwater cruisers.

Sinking the *Belgrano*

Their main combat arena lies under the Arctic ice cap; but the crew of HMS *Conqueror* went to war in very different circumstances. One of three Churchill-class nuclear-powered attack submarines (SSNs), HMS *Conqueror* was the boat that sank the Argentinian cruiser *General Belgrano* on 2 May 1982, at the start of the Falklands War. The Churchills were modified Valiant-class SSNs and were somewhat quieter in service, having benefited from the experience gained in operating the earlier boats. When the Churchills were first built their main armament was the Mk 8 anti-ship torpedo of World War II vintage, and it was a salvo of these that sank the *Belgrano*. The armament was later updated to include the Mk24 Tigerfish wire-guided dual-role (anti-ship and anti-submarine) torpedo, the Sub-Harpoon SSM and a new generation of 'smart' mines. The Churchills and their predecessors, *Valiant* and *Warspite*, were paid off in the late 1980s, following the full deployment of the Trafalgar-class SSNs.

Today, nuclear attack submarines are armed with cruise missiles, and have launched these in combat against targets in Iraq and elsewhere.

Downes

The purpose of the US Navy's Knox-class frigates, to which the USS *Downes* belongs, was to act as escorts for convoys and amphibious task forces, and they were much less specialized than the traditional ASW frigates.

COUNTRY: USA

TYPE: Frigate

LAUNCH DATE: 13 December 1969

CREW: 220

DISPLACEMENT: 4165 tonnes (4100 tons)

DIMENSIONS: 126.6m x 14m x 7.5m (415ft 4in x 46ft 9in x 24ft 7in)

RANGE: 8338km (4500nm)

MAIN ARMAMENT: One 127mm (5in) gun; one eight-tube Sea Sparrow missile launcher; Phalanx CIWS

POWERPLANT: Single screw, turbines

PERFORMANCE: 27 knots

After many years of service, the USS *Downes*, pictured here in her heyday, was sunk as a target ship in 1992.

At the time of their building, the 46 Knox-class ocean escorts, of which *Downes* was one, comprised the largest group of destroyer-escort type warships built to the same design in the West since World War II. The ships were almost identical to the earlier Garcia and Brooke classes, but slightly larger. Original planning provided for the vessels to have the Sea Mauler, a short-range anti-aircraft missile adapted from a missile being developed by the US Army, but the Mauler/Sea Mauler programme was abandoned because of technical difficulties.

Weapons and sensor testing

Beginning in 1980 and onwards the ships were taken in hand to receive raised bulwarks and strakes forward to improve their seakeeping in heavy weather. Numerous Knoxes were used over the years to test individual prototype weapon and sensor systems. Thirty-seven were equipped with a multiple Sea Sparrow launcher, but this was later replaced by the Phalanx Close-in Warfare System. The ships had a very large superstructure and a distinctive cylindrical structure combining masts and engine exhaust stacks.

Although specialized ASW vessels, the Knox-class frigates were intended primarily for convoy protection work.

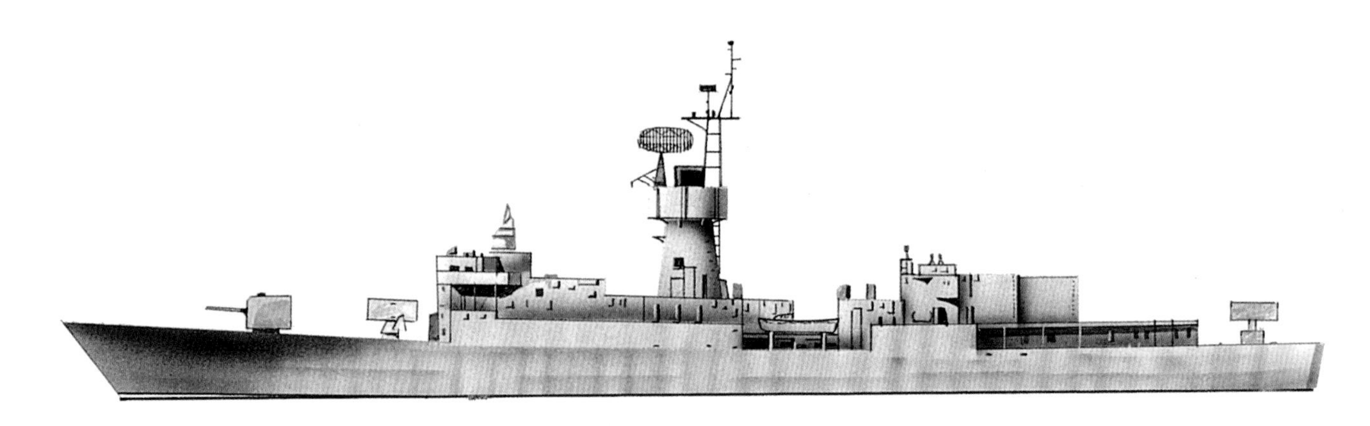

Delta Class

Until the early 1970s, the USA led the world in highly sophisticated and effective nuclear-missile submarines. Then the Russians deployed a new class of ballistic-missile submarine, the *Delta I*, or Murena-class SSBN.

COUNTRY: Soviet Union
TYPE: Ballistic–missile submarine
LAUNCH DATE: 1971
CREW: 120
DISPLACEMENT: Submerged: 11,176 tonnes (11,000 tons)
DIMENSIONS: 150m x 12m x 10.2m (492ft x 39ft 4in x 33ft 6in)
RANGE: Unlimited
ARMAMENT: Twelve missile tubes, six 457mm (18in) torpedo tubes
POWERPLANT: Nuclear, two reactors
PERFORMANCE: Surfaced: 19 knots, submerged: 25 knots

At the time of its appearance, the *Delta* was the most formidable submarine in the Soviet Navy's arsenal.

The Delta class was a major improvement on the earlier Yankee class and was armed with missiles that could outrange the US *Poseidon*. Each boat had 12 two-stage SS-N-8 missiles. The first Delta was laid down at Severodvinsk in 1969, launched in 1971 and finished in 1972. With the end of the Cold War and rapidly shrinking naval budgets, the first of the class was paid off in 1992: all have now been withdrawn from service, including the Delta II class. These were essentially Delta Is with a extra 9m (30ft) length of hull added to allow them to carry four SS-N-8 more missiles. The Delta III- or Kalmar-class SSBN, completed between 1976 and 1982, had some visible differences to the earlier Delta II class from which it evolved, the most noticeable being that the missile casing was higher in order to accommodate the SS-N-18 missiles, which are longer than the SS-N-8s of the Delta II.

The last of the Deltas

The last of the class is the Delta IV, construction of which was first ordered in December 1975. The first of eight boats was launched and commissioned in 1984 at Severodvinsk and the programme was completed in late 1990.

The sinister black shapes of the Delta–class submarines were rarely seen on the surface once they had left their polar bases on patrol.

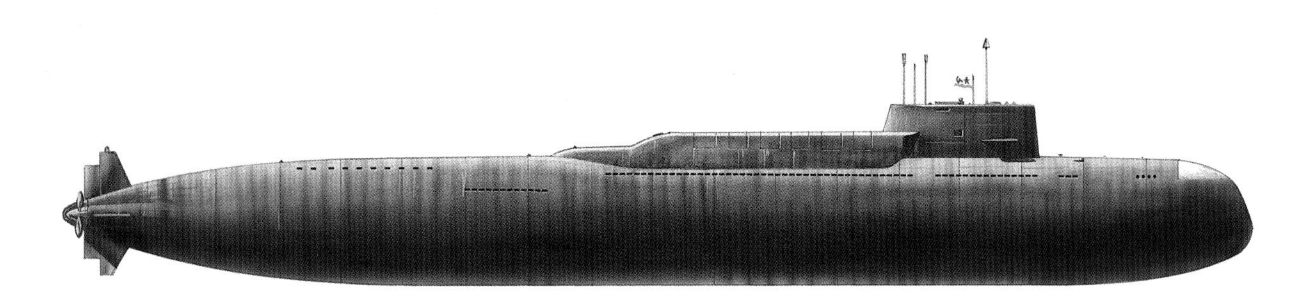

Han

In the 1970s, the Chinese Navy made a determined effort to deploy equipment, including nuclear submarines, that brought it on to a more modern footing, but its technological expertise did not match its requirements.

COUNTRY: China

TYPE: Attack submarine

LAUNCH DATE: 1972

CREW: 120

DISPLACEMENT: Surfaced: not known, submerged: 5080 tonnes (5000 tons)

DIMENSIONS: 90m x 8m x 8.2m (295ft 3in x 26ft 3in x 27ft)

RANGE: Unlimited

ARMAMENT: Six 533mm (21in) torpedo tubes

POWERPLANT: Single screw, pressurized water nuclear reactor

PERFORMANCE: Surfaced: 20 knots, submerged: 28 knots

This splendid view of a Han-class nuclear submarine on the surface of the Pacific was taken by a US Navy patrol aircraft.

The Chinese Navy took a massive leap forward in the early 1970s with its Han-class nuclear-attack submarines (SSNs). The highly streamlined hull shape was based on the design of the USS *Albacore*. While the Russians cut many corners to get their first SSNs into service, China proceeded at a more leisurely pace, and although the Han class of four boats is fairly basic, with little of the high technology that is standard on American and British vessels, it provided a solid basis for further development. From the Hans came the Xia class, China's first nuclear ballistic-missile submarine. At least one of the Han class was modified during construction to carry CSS-N-2 missile tubes.

Problems were encountered during this missile's protracted development, but many of these were corrected in the following two-stage solid-propellant CSS-N-3, which was first test-fired in October 1982. The definitive solid-fuel derivative was the CSS-N-4, designated Julang-1 (Great Wave I).

Keeping accidents secret

According to some reports, however, China's SSN/SSBN programme has suffered its fair share of accidents, which have been concealed from the rest of the world.

The Han-class submarines provided a base for further development.

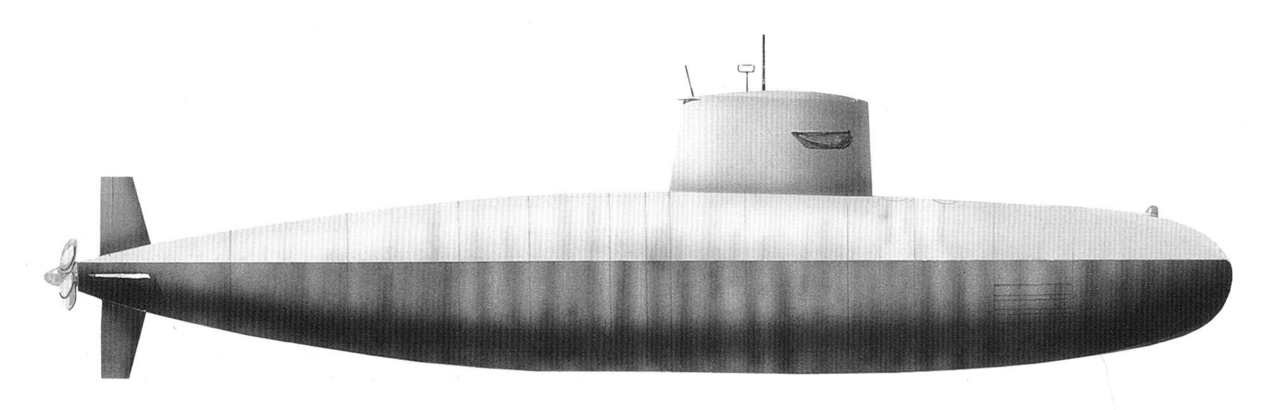

Kiev

The *Kiev* came as a surprise to NATO when she emerged from the Black Sea and passed through the Mediterranean to join the Soviet Northern Fleet. She and her sister ships now formed the core of powerful surface action groups.

Kiev was the first Soviet aircraft carrier to be built with a full flight deck and a purpose-built hull. She was laid down in September 1970 in the Black Sea Nikolayev Dockyard and completed in May 1975. The flight deck is angled, with most of the armament carried forward. Twenty-four of the SS-N-12 Shaddock-type missiles were carried. The large bridge structure is set on *Kiev*'s starboard side, and housed an array of radar equipment. The ship joined the Soviet Northern Fleet in 1976. *Kiev* carried an air group of Yakovlev Yak-38 Forger VTOL fighter-bombers and anti-submarine helicopters. The normal complement for the Kiev-class through-deck aircraft carrier was a dozen single-seat Forger-As and one or two twin-seat trainer Yak-38U Forger-Bs.

The *Kiev* pictured with some of her Yak-38 Forger V/STOL strike aircraft and Hormone ASW helicopters on deck.

COUNTRY:	Soviet Union
TYPE:	Aircraft carrier
LAUNCH DATE:	26 December 1972
CREW:	1700
DISPLACEMENT:	38,608 tonnes (38,000 tons)
DIMENSIONS:	273m x 47.2m x 8.2m (895ft 8in x 154ft 10in x 27ft)
RANGE:	24,300km (13,500nm) at 10 knots
ARMAMENT:	Four 76.2mm (3in) guns, plus up to 136 missiles
POWERPLANT:	Quadruple screw turbines
PERFORMANCE:	32 knots

The primary roles were fleet defence (particularly against shadowing maritime surveillance aircraft), reconnaissance and anti-ship strike. The Forger was retired from front-line service in 1992-3, although a few remained in the inventory for another year as limited proficiency training aircraft.

Museum piece

Kiev was donated to China as a museum piece. Other vessels in the Kiev class were *Minsk*, *Novorossiysk* (both stricken) and *Admiral Gorshkov*, which has been refitted and sold to India.

The *Kiev* was well armed with anti-ship and anti-aircraft missiles, but her Yak-38s were not in the same league as the V/STOL Harrier.

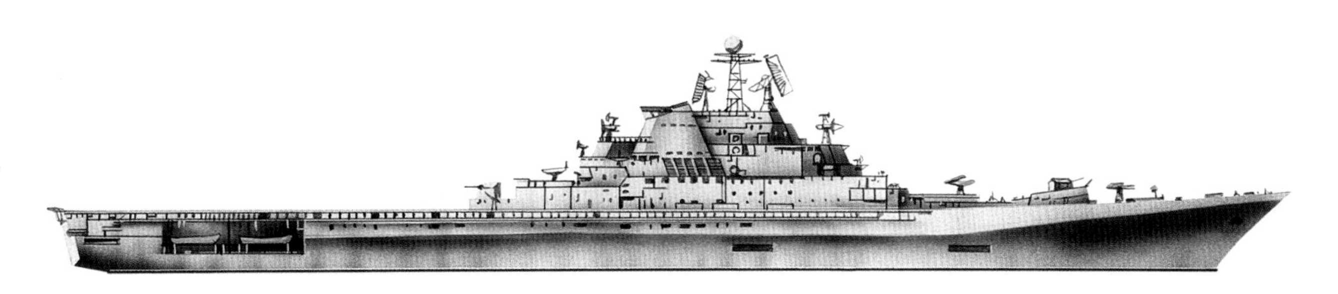

Krivak class

The Krivak-class frigates showed how far the Soviet Union had come in building up an immensely powerful 'blue water' fleet since the days of the early 1960s, when the Soviet Navy held its first tentative out-of-area exercises.

COUNTRY: Soviet Union
TYPE: Frigate
LAUNCH DATE: 1975 (Rezvyy)
CREW: 220
DISPLACEMENT: 3759 tonnes (3700 tons)
DIMENSIONS: 123.5m x 14m x 4.7m (405ft 2in x 45ft 11in x 15ft 5in)
RANGE: 5188km (2800nm)
MAIN ARMAMENT: Two single 100mm (3.9in) DP guns; SAMs; ASW missiles; eight 533mm (21in) torpedo tubes
POWERPLANT: Two shafts, four gas turbines
PERFORMANCE: 32 knots

The *Krivak* appeared to be a formidable frigate when it made its appearance, but it had limited endurance.

In 1970 the first unit of the Krivak I class of large anti-submarine warfare vessels entered service with the Soviet Navy. Built between 1971–82, 21 units of this variant were constructed. In 1976 the Krivak II class, of which 11 were built, was the first seen. This differed from the previous class in having single 100mm (3.9in) guns substituted for the twin 76mm (3in) turrets of the earlier version, and a larger, variable-depth sonar at the stern.

Patrol ship status

The Krivak II was much in evidence in April 1980, when the Russians conducted an exercise in which Kiev-class ship *Novorossiysk* left the Mediterranean en route for the Northern Fleet. Three Krivak-class frigates departed the Baltic and joined the *Novorossiysk* group to the west of Land's End. The units conducted anti-submarine warfare operations west of Ireland with three submarines located in the area. The Krivaks then entered the Mediterranean while the carrier group continued north, simulating air-to-surface strikes en route. Both classes were re-rated to patrol ship status in the late 1970s, possibly in the light of what some observers considered to be deficiencies in terms of limited endurance for ASW operations in open waters. An improved Krivak III class was later developed, and three export versions have been sold to India.

The *Krivak* was a powerful addition to the USSR's anti-submarine warfare forces.

Broadsword

The Broadsword-class frigates operated in the Falklands War of 1982 and the first Gulf War of 1991, acting in the 'goalkeeper' role as protectors of naval task forces, and armed with the British Aerospace Sea Wolf missiles.

COUNTRY: Great Britain
TYPE: Frigate
LAUNCH DATE: 12 May 1976
CREW: 286
DISPLACEMENT: 4470 tonnes (4400 tons)
DIMENSIONS 131m x 14.8m x 4.2m (430ft 5in x 48ft 8in x 14ft)
RANGE: 7408km (4000nm)
MAIN ARMAMENT: Four M38 Exocet launchers; two 30mm (1.6in) guns; two sextuple Sea Wolf SAM; Sting Ray torpedoes
POWERPLANT: Twin screw gas turbine engines
PERFORMANCE: 30 knots

HMS *Broadsword* at anchor on the Thames. The class proved very effective in its anti-aircraft role.

The British Leander class of frigate, which entered service in the 1960s, served the Royal Navy for many years; 26 were built. The Leanders were to have been succeeded by 26 examples of the Type 22 Broadsword class, conceived as ASW ships for use in the Greenland–Iceland–UK gap against Soviet high-performance nuclear submarines, but in the event only 14 were built.

Three Batches

Brilliant and *Broadsword* distinguished themselves in action during the 1982 Falklands War. All the Batch 1 vessels were sold to Brazil: *Broadsword* on 30 June 1995, *Brilliant* and *Brazen* on 30 August 1996, and *Battleaxe* on 30 April 1997. The Batch 2 Broadswords, *Boxer*, *Beaver*, *Brave*, *London*, *Sheffield* and *Coventry*, have now all been decommissioned. The Broadswords were built in three batches, of which Batch 3 was a general-purpose variant, and all have enlarged flight decks for the operation of Sea King or EH101 Merlin helicopters, although a single Westland Lynx is usually embarked for peacetime operations. The Batch 3 ships are fitted with two Rolls-Royce Spey SM1A and two Rolls-Royce Tyne gas turbines; the more powerful Spey SM1C engines might be retrofitted in due course.

The Broadsword class were highly capable warships developed in response to the USSR's growing air-to-surface anti-ship capability.

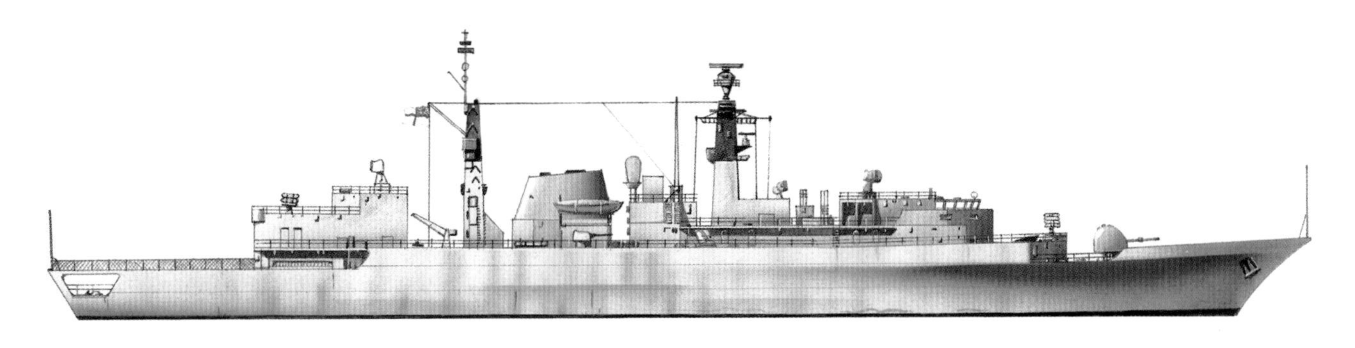

Oliver Hazard Perry

Destined to be numerically the largest warship class in the US Navy, the Oliver Hazard Perry class was designed for anti-air warfare with ASW and anti-surface warfare as secondary roles.

The Oliver Hazard Perry-class frigates were deployed in response to the USSR's ability to attack NATO surface vessels at long range.

COUNTRY:	USA
TYPE:	Frigate
LAUNCH DATE:	25 September 1976
CREW:	215
DISPLACEMENT:	3717 tonnes (3658 tons)
DIMENSIONS:	135.6m x 13.7m x 4.5m (445ft x 45ft x 14ft 10in)
RANGE:	10,371km (5600nm)
MAIN ARMAMENT:	One 76mm (3in) DP gun; two triple 324mm (12.75in) torpedo tubes; Harpoon SSMs and Standard ASMs
POWERPLANT:	Single shaft, two gas turbines
PERFORMANCE:	29 knots

The USS *Oliver Hazard Perry* was the first of a class of 51 frigates designed to escort merchant convoys or amphibious squadrons. Their primary role was to provide area defence of surface forces against attacking aircraft and cruise missiles, with anti-surface warfare as secondary role.

RAST System

The class leader was named for Oliver Hazard Perry, a US naval hero. Ordered as part of the FY73 programme, *Oliver Hazard Perry* was laid down on 12 June 1975, launched on 25 September 1976, and commissioned on 17 December 1977. She was ordered as PFG-109 but redesignated FFG-7 in the 1975 fleet designation realignment, before she was laid down. She was decommissioned on 20 February 1997 and stricken on 3 May 1999. Because of cost considerations, the first 26 ships were not retrofitted to carry two LAMPS III ASW helicopters, as planned, but retained the LAMPS I. LAMPS facilities include the Recovery Assistance, Security and Traversing (RAST) system which allows the launch and recovery of the Sikorsky SH-60 helicopters with the ship rolling through 28 degrees and pitching up to 5 degrees. Two ships of this class, the *Stark* and *Samuel B. Roberts*, were damaged in missile attacks while patrolling the Arabian Gulf during the Iraq–Iran war in 1987 and 1988.

Capable of carrying out a variety of tasks, the Oliver Hazard Perry class were very much in the nature of 'workhorse' warships.

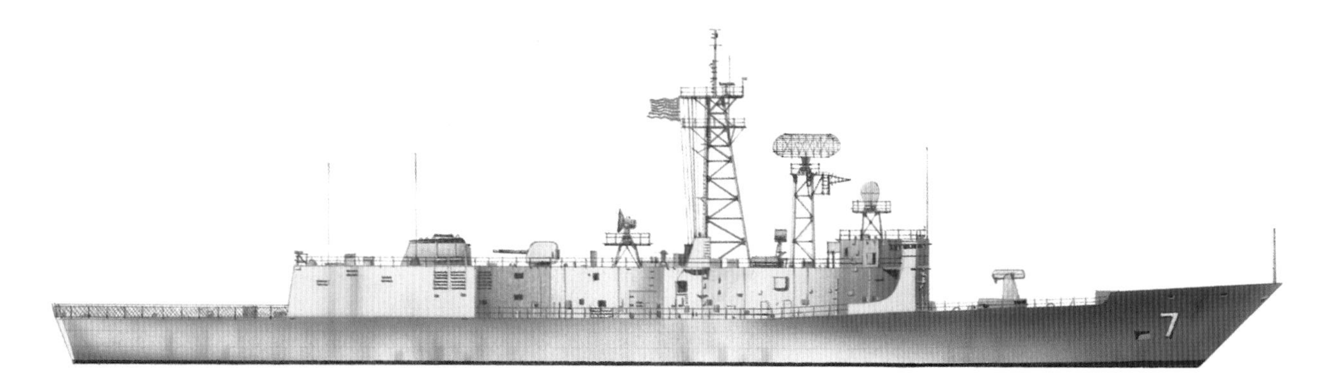

Exeter

The combination of HMS *Exeter* and her Sea Dart missiles proved very effective in the Falklands War of 1982, the missiles shooting down two Argentine Skyhawks and two reconnaissance aircraft.

COUNTRY: Great Britain	
TYPE: Destroyer	
LAUNCH DATE: 25 April 1978	
CREW: 253	
DISPLACEMENT: 4166 tonnes (4100 tons)	
DIMENSIONS: 125m x 14.3m x 5.8m (412ft x 47ft x 19ft)	
RANGE: 6430km (3472nm)	
MAIN ARMAMENT: One 114mm (4.5in) gun; Sea Dart SAM; 20mm (0.7in) and Phalanx AA	
POWERPLANT: Twin shafts, four gas turbines	
PERFORMANCE: 29 knots	

HMS *Exeter* pictured with her Westland Lynx helicopter on the helipad. The Type 42 destroyers were designed for the fleet defence role.

HMS *Exeter*, launched in April 1978 and commissioned in September 1980, is one of four Batch 2 Type 42 destroyers, the others being *Southampton*, *Nottingham* and *Liverpool*. The Type 42s were originally designed to provide area defence for a task force with their British Aerospace Sea Dart surface-to-air missiles; these have a range of 40km (21.5nm) under radar or semi-active radar guidance and have a height envelope of 100–18,300m (328–60,042ft). The weapons also have a limited anti-ship capability.

Active in the Falklands and the Gulf

Generally, each Type 42 is armed with 22 Sea Dart rounds. The ships' Lynx helicopter carries the Sea Skua air-to-surface missile for use against lightly defended surface-ship targets, and has been operationally proved in the Falklands and Gulf conflicts, being especially effective against small, fast targets. Early in her first commission, *Exeter* had a turquoise hull; this was an experimental co-polymer paint only available in a few non-standard colours. The experiment was successful and the ship's hull was repainted to standard brick red/black during its first docking period, after the Falklands campaign. She was to have patrolled the North Atlantic and European waters, but the then Defence Secretary issued his review of the Armed forces, which seriously restricted her future operational deployments.

All Type 42 destroyers carried a Lynx helicopter, as seen in this illustration.

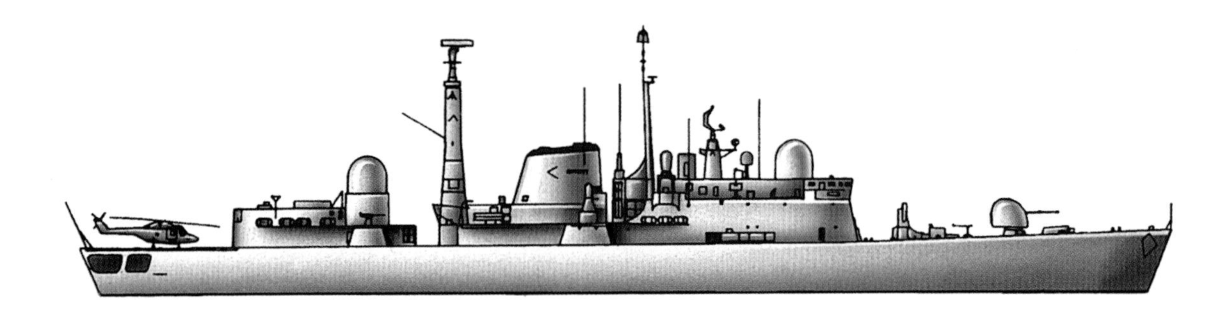

Cassard

***Cassard* and her sister ship *Jean Bart* are optimized for anti-aircraft warfare, and form an important element of French naval task forces.**

COUNTRY: France
TYPE: Destroyer
LAUNCH DATE: 6 February 1985
CREW: 225
DISPLACEMENT: 4806 tonnes (4730 tons)
DIMENSIONS: 139m x 14m x 6.5m (455ft 11in x 45ft 9in x 21ft 3in)
RANGE: 13,182km (7118nm)
MAIN ARMAMENT: One 100mm (3.9in) gun; Exocet; Mistral anti-sea-skimming missiles; standard SAMs; ASW torpedoes
POWERPLANT: Two shafts, four diesel engines
PERFORMANCE: 29.5 knots

***Cassard* pictured in the Adriatic during operations in support of French UN forces operating in the Balkans.**

Four destroyers of the Cassard class were originally laid down, but two were subsequently cancelled. The *Cassard* and her sister ship, *Jean Bart*, were laid down in September 1982 and March 1986 respectively at the Lorient Naval Dockyard, and commissioned in July 1988 and September 1991. The building programme was subjected to serious delays because of financial constraints and doubts about the effectiveness of the increasingly obsolescent Standard SM-1 surface-to-air missile system; there are plans to replace this with the Aster 30 system as the ships are refitted. The radar and countermeasures equipment carried by the two ships is of French design. The ships have a helicopter platform at the stern for use by a single Aerospatiale Panther (now replacing the Lynx).

An escort ship

Both ships are based at Toulon. In 1999, *Cassard* escorted the French aircraft carrier *Foch* in the Adriatic while *Foch*'s aircraft were engaged in operations against objectives in the former Yugoslavia. In 2002 and 2006, *Cassard* carried out a similar function in the Indian Ocean, escorting the nuclear-powered aircraft carrier *Charles de Gaulle*, whose aircraft were operating against terrorist targets in Afghanistan as part of Operation Enduring Freedom. In 2006, she was also involved in evacuation operations off the Lebanon, where Israeli forces were fighting Hezbollah.

In 2000–1 *Cassard* was fitted with external bulges, 100 tons of ballast being added to enhance stability.

Admiral Kuznetsov

Launched in 1985 and described as a heavy aircraft-carrying cruiser by Russia, the *Admiral Kuznetsov* is the only aircraft carrier in the Russian Navy. She was originally named *Tbilisi*, and then *Leonid Brezhnev*.

COUNTRY: USSR	
TYPE: Aircraft carrier	
LAUNCH DATE: December 5, 1985	
CREW: 1960	
DISPLACEMENT: 53,000–55,000 tonnes standard	
DIMENSIONS: 300m x 73m x 11m (984ft x 238ft x 36ft)	
RANGE: 7100km (3834nm) at 32 knots	
ARMAMENT: Guns: 8 x AK-630 AA: CADS-1 CIWS Kashtan CIWS gun and missile system : Missiles: 12 x P-700 Granit SSM 18 x 8-cell 3K95 Kinzhal SAM : ASW:2 x RBU-12000 UDAV-1 ASW rocket launchers	
POWERPLANT: Steam turbines, 8 boilers, 4 shafts, 149 MW 2x37mW turbines, 9x1500 kW turbogenerators, 6x1500 kW diesel generators	
PERFORMANCE: 32 knots	

The design of the *Kuznetsov*'s hull is based on that of an earlier vessel, the *Admiral Gorshkov*, which was withdrawn from service in 1988 and sold to India. Renamed INS *Vikramaditya*, she was due to enter service with the Indian Navy in 2008.

Missile system details

Admiral Kuznetsov's air group comprises 12 Sukhoi Su-27 Flanker fixed-wing interceptor/strike aircraft and up to 24 helicopters. She is armed with a Granit anti-ship missile system equipped with 12 surface-to-surface missile launchers. The Granit missile is reported to have a range greater than 400km (250 miles) and carries either a nuclear or conventional warhead. Primary defence against anti-ship missiles and aircraft is the Klinok air defence missile system, with 24 vertical launchers and 192 missiles. The system has a multi-channel electronically steered phased array radar with a firing rate of one missile every three seconds. Four targets can be engaged at once at a range of 12–15km (7–9 miles) away. A second Kuznetsov-class vessel, the *Varyag*, was ordered but never commissioned. Acquired by the Ukraine, where she was building at the time of the break-up of the Soviet Union, she was later sold to the People's Republic of China on the condition that she would never be fitted out for combat.

***Admiral Kuznetsov* was a bold attempt by the former Soviet Union to form a modern surface action group based on a viable aircraft carrier.**

The *Admiral Kuznetsov* has a distinctive silhouette. Her air group includes a dozen Su-27 fighter-bombers.

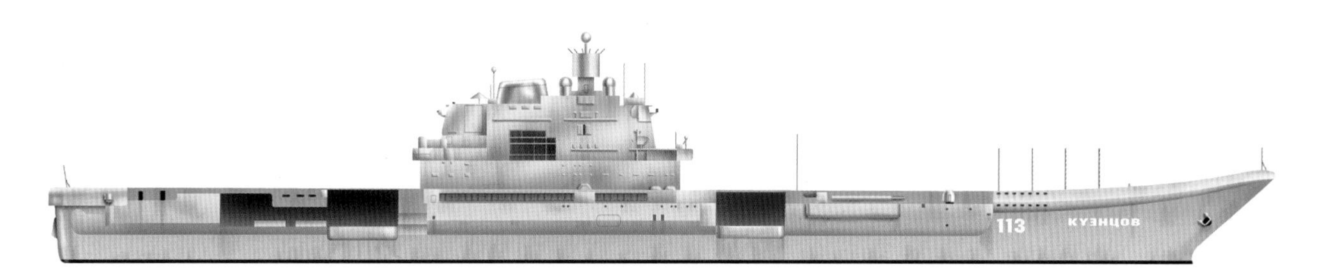

Torbay

Laid down in December 1982, launched in March 1985 and commissioned in February 1987, *Torbay* was the fourth of seven Trafalgar-class attack submarines, an advanced derivative of the previous Swiftsure class.

COUNTRY: United Kingdom
TYPE: Submarine
LAUNCH DATE: March 1987
CREW: 97
DISPLACEMENT: 4700t surfaced; 5200t submerged
DIMENSIONS: 85.4m x 9.8m x 9.5m (280ft 2in x 32ft 2in x 31ft 3in)
RANGE: Limited only by reactor fuel state
ARMAMENT: Five 21in (533mm) TT (maximum of 21 Tigerfish torpedoes, four Sub-Harpoon anti-ship missiles)
POWERPLANT: one-shaft, nuclear, one PWR1 reactor with two geared steam turbines, one diesel-electric auxiliary motor and two batteries; 15,000hp/4000hp
PERFORMANCE: 20 knots surfaced; 30 knots submerged

HMS *Torbay* is pictured here under construction. She was the fifth vessel to carry the name.

The Trafalgar-class submarines formed the backbone of the Royal Navy's ASW capability, detecting, identifying and stalking enemy submarines yet remaining undetected. Exceptionally quiet, the Trafalgars are covered with conformal anechoic tiles and have retractable foreplanes and a strengthened fin for under-ice operations.

Multiple capabilities

They are also capable of operating at extreme depths, some sources quoting 500m (1640ft). Armed with Mk 24 Tigerfish wire-guided torpedoes, fired from five bow tubes, four UGM-84A anti-ship missiles or submarine-launched cruise missiles, the Trafalgar class boats also have a powerful capability against targets on land, and can also be used for surveillance. While early boats in the class had a seven-bladed propeller, *Torbay* and some of her sister boats have a shrouded propulsor instead. The Trafalgar-class boats serve with the 2nd Submarine Squadron at Devonport. Two are usually in refit at any given time.

The Trafalgars were extensively modified in the 1990s, receiving upgraded sonar equipment, Spearfish torpedoes and cruise missiles.

Arleigh Burke

The *Arleigh Burke* class of fleet escorts (destroyers) augment the US Navy's larger Ticonderoga class of escort cruisers in the protection of US carrier battle groups.

COUNTRY: USA
TYPE: Guided-missile destroyer
LAUNCH DATE: 16 September 1989
CREW: 303
DISPLACEMENT: 8534 tonnes (8400 tons)
DIMENSIONS: 81m x 18.3m x 9.1m (266ft 3in x 60ft x 30ft)
RANGE: 11,118km (6000nm)
MAIN ARMAMENT: Harpoon and Tomahawk anti-ship and land attack cruise missiles; one 127mm (5in) gun.
POWERPLANT: Twin shaft gas turbine
PERFORMANCE: 32 knots

Despite their relatively small size, the Arleigh Burke-class destroyers are among the most powerful warships afloat.

This large class of guided-missile destroyer was designed to replace the ageing Adams- and Coontz-class destroyers, which entered service in the early 1960s. The principal mission of the Arleigh Burke class is to provide effective anti-aircraft cover, for which they have the SPY 1D version of the Aegis area defence system.

Heavily protected ships

The Arleigh Burkes are the first US warships to be fully equipped for warfare in a nuclear, chemical or biological environment, the crew being confined in a citadel located within the hull and superstructure. Plastic Kevlar armour covers all vital machinery and operations room spaces. Armament includes one 127mm (5in) DP gun and two 20mm Phalanx CIWS mountings, and there is a platform for an ASW helicopter along with a laser designator for the guidance of the DP gun's Deadeye shells. The first vessel in the class, the USS *Arleigh Burke*, was laid down in December 1988, launched in September 1989 and completed in 1991. The Arleigh Burkes are armed with two Mk 41 vertical launch systems for Tomahawk land attack cruise missiles, Harpoon anti-ship missiles and Standard SM-2MR surface-to-air missiles.

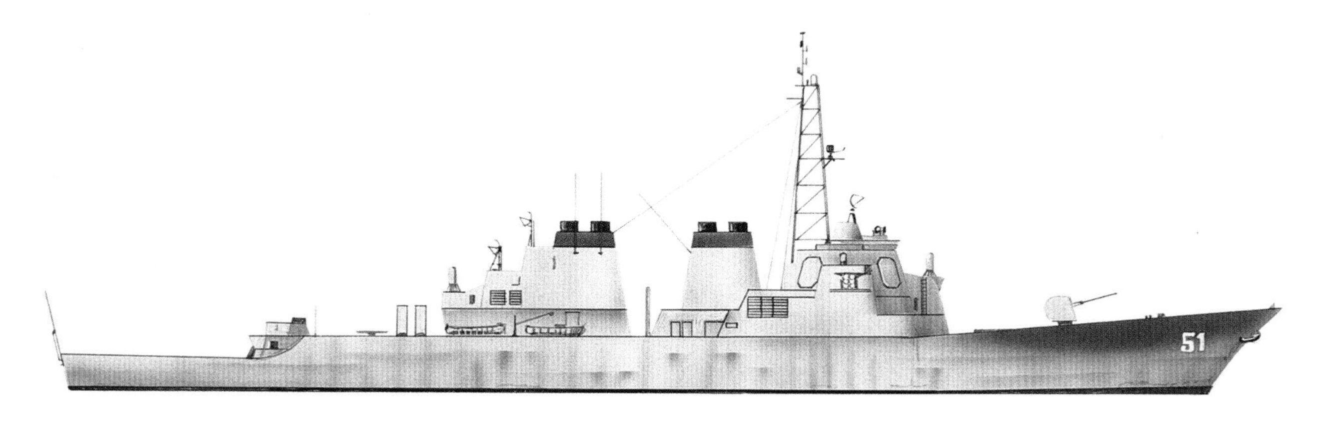

The electronic arrays for the *Arleigh Burke*'s SPY-1 radars are visible as flat panels on its forward superstructure.

Harbin

***Harbin* was first publicly revealed in 1996 near the Taiwan Strait. On 21 March 1997 the destroyer and two other Chinese warships made the first-ever visit by People's Republic of China Navy ships to the mainland USA.**

COUNTRY: China

TYPE: Destroyer

LAUNCH DATE: October 1991

CREW: 230

DISPLACEMENT: 4267 tonnes (4200 tons)

DIMENSIONS: 142.7m x 15.1m x 5.1m (468ft 2in x 49ft 6in x 16ft 8in)

RANGE: 8042km (4340nm)

MAIN ARMAMENT: Two 100mm (3.9in) guns; YJ-1 Eagle Strike SSMs; 324mm (12.75in) torpedo tubes

POWERPLANT: Two shafts, two gas turbines, two diesels

PERFORMANCE: 31 knots

The *Harbin* pictured at San Diego during her historic visit to the United States in 1997.

Harbin was the first of a class of two destroyers (the other was the *Qingdao*) ordered in 1985. Construction was delayed because priority had already been given to warship construction for Thailand, and the vessels were not commissioned until 1994 and 1996 respectively. Notable features are the forward-mounted octuple launcher for the HQ-7 (Crotale) SAM system, improved radar and fire-control systems, and a twin 100mm (3.9in) gun that fires a 15kg (33lb) shell up to 22km (12nm). *Harbin* is based with the North Sea Fleet at Guzhen Bay, while *Qingdao* is with the East Sea Fleet at Jianggezhuang. The gas turbines for the latter warship were built in the Ukraine. Chinese warships have frequently been criticized for poor quality of construction.

Harbin was the largest surface warship in service with the PLA Navy when she was commissioned.

Improved but still lagging behind

Despite its various improvements compared to previous Chinese-built surface combatants, the Harbin class still lagged behind Western- and Russian-built warships of the same vintage. The ship's air defence firepower, consisting of a 13km-range Crotale/HQ-7 air defence missile launcher and four twin-37mm AAA guns, is only capable of point defence against a limited number of targets, while the variable depth sonar (VDS) is still inferior to the latest Western designs. Additionally, the shipborne Z-9C naval helicopter has only very limited anti-submarine warfare capability.

HMS Ocean

The assault ship HMS *Ocean* was launched on 11 October 1995. She is the sixth ship to bear the name, her most recent ancestor being a light fleet carrier, also built on the Clyde and commissioned on 30 June 1945.

COUNTRY: UK
TYPE: Landing platform, helicopter
LAUNCH DATE: 11 October 1995
CREW: 800
DISPLACEMENT: 19,575 tonnes (21,578 tons)
DIMENSIONS: 208m x 34.4 x 6.6m (682ft x 113ft x 21ft 6in)
RANGE: 12,875km (8000 miles)
ARMAMENT: 3 x Phalanx CIWS
POWERPLANT: 2 x Crossley Pielstick diesel engines; 1 x Kamewa bow thruster
PERFORMANCE: 18 knots

HMS *Ocean* provides the Royal Navy with a modern and effective assault capability.

HMS *Ocean* was commissioned on 30 September 1998, completing her trials programme and initial basic operational sea training in the spring of 1999.

Amphibious assault capabilities

The Amphibious Helicopter Carrier was originally conceived in the mid–1980s to provide the sort of amphibious assault capabilities last offered by HMS *Albion* and HMS *Bulwark*. The ship's primary role is to carry an Embarked Military Force (EMF) supported by 12 medium support helicopters, 6 attack helicopters and 4 Landing Craft Vehicle Personnel (LCVP) Mk 5 Landing Craft. Her secondary roles include afloat training, a limited anti-submarine warfare (ASW) platform and a base for anti-terrorist operations. Vehicles and stores are loaded through a starboard quarter ramp, and the deck can take six 105mm howitzer light guns and up to 40 assorted military vehicles. A ramp from the vehicle deck to the flight deck allows equipment to be flown ashore by helicopter. At anchor vehicles can also be unloaded through the ship's stern ramp on to Mexiflotes, then transferred ashore.

By no means an attractive vessel, HMS *Ocean*'s design reflects her primary function of helicopter-borne assault ship.

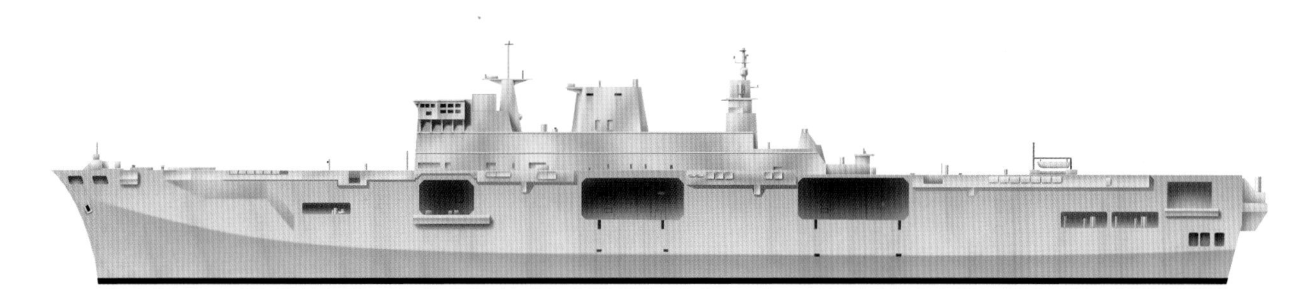

USS Ronald Reagan

The USS *Ronald Reagan* is the ninth of the mighty USS Nimitz-class supercarriers, the first of which was launched in 1969. Their nuclear reactors have a life of about 15 years, and they carry an air group of 85 aircraft.

COUNTRY: US
TYPE: Supercarrier
LAUNCH DATE: 4 March 2001
CREW: 3,200
DISPLACEMENT: 91,625–94.350 tonnes (101,000–104,000 tons)
DIMENSIONS: Length: 333m (1092 ft)
RANGE: Unlimited
ARMAMENT: 2 Mk 29 Sea Sparrow, 2 RIM-116 Rolling Airframe Missile
POWERPLANT: 2 Westinghouse A4W nuclear reactors, 4 steam turbines, 4 shafts 260,000 shp (194 MW)
PERFORMANCE: 30+ knots

Launched in 2001, the *Ronald Reagan* displaces some 95,000 tons fully loaded, and can sail for 20 years before the reactors must be refuelled. At 333m (1092ft) long, and with a complement of over 5500 sailors she is the size of a small town. Her air wing strike component comprises four squadrons of F/A-18C Hornets and F/A-18E Super Hornets; other aircraft include the E-2C Hawkeye early warning aircraft and the SH-60F/HH-60H Blackhawk helicopter. Operationally, the USS *Ronald Reagan* is the flagship of Carrier Strike Group 7 (CSG-7), which also includes three guided-missile destroyers and a fast combat support ship. On her maiden voyage in 2006 her strike aircraft conducted operations against terrorist targets in Afghanistan. Her home port is Coronado, California.

Named (just in time) after a living personality

At the time of her launch in 2001 the USS *Ronald Reagan* was one of the very few ships in the US Navy to have been named after a personality who was still living. She was launched by Mrs Nancy Reagan, the former US President being unable to attend because of Alzheimer's disease. He died 11 months later.

The USS *Ronald Reagan* travelling at speed with 'a bone in her teeth', to use a nautical expression.

For a vessel of her size the USS *Ronald Reagan* has quite a rakish appearance, as is apparent in this illustration.

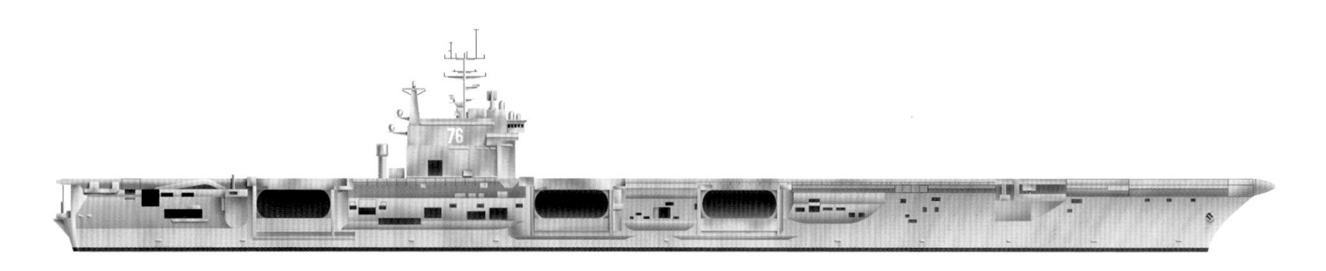

HMS Daring

Launched on 1 February 2006, the Type 45 destroyer HMS *Daring* is scheduled to enter service in 2009. She is the first of six similar vessels, the others being HMS *Dauntless*, *Diamond*, *Defender*, *Dragon* and *Duncan*.

COUNTRY: UK
TYPE: Air-defence warship
LAUNCH DATE: 1 February 2006
CREW: 190
DISPLACEMENT: 7350 tonnes (8102 tons)
DIMENSIONS: Length:152.4m (500ft), Beam: 21.2m (69ft 6in), Draught: 5.0m (16ft)
RANGE: 13,000km (7000nm) at economical speed
ARMAMENT: 2 Phalanx CIWS BAE Systems 114mm (4.5in) Mk 8 Mod. 1 gun, 2 x 30mm guns
POWERPLANT: 2 Rolls-Royce WR-21 gas turbines, Alstom electric motors
PERFORMANCE: 29+ knots

HMS *Daring* seen during the final phase of her construction at BAe Systems' Scotstoun yard.

Daring successfully completed her stage-one sea trials in 2007. The Type 45 Anti-Air Warfare Destroyers will provide the backbone of the Royal Navy's air defences for the first half of the twenty-first century, able to engage a large number of targets simultaneously and defend aircraft carriers or groups of ships, such as an amphibious landing force, against the strongest future threats from the air.

Specialist air-warfare capability

A versatile warship, the Type 45 will provide unprecedented detection and defence and will contribute to worldwide maritime and joint operations in multi-threat environments, providing a specialist air-warfare capability. Its main armament is the Principal Anti-Air Missile System (PAAMS), a surface-to-air missile system developed under a tri-national programme by France, Italy and the UK. This advanced weapon system will defend the Type 45, her consorts and other task-force vessels against highly manoeuvrable hostile incoming aircraft and missiles approaching at subsonic and supersonic speed, individually or in salvoes. The Type 45 could also accommodate cruise missiles such as the Tomahawk and anti-ballistic missiles if a requirement should be identified in the future. The Type 45 will be able to operate a helicopter up to the size of a Royal Navy Merlin, but will initially operate with Lynx HMA.8 helicopters armed with Stingray torpedoes.

A highly functional and ultra-modern warships, *Daring* brings an enormous boost to the Royal Navy's surface fleet.

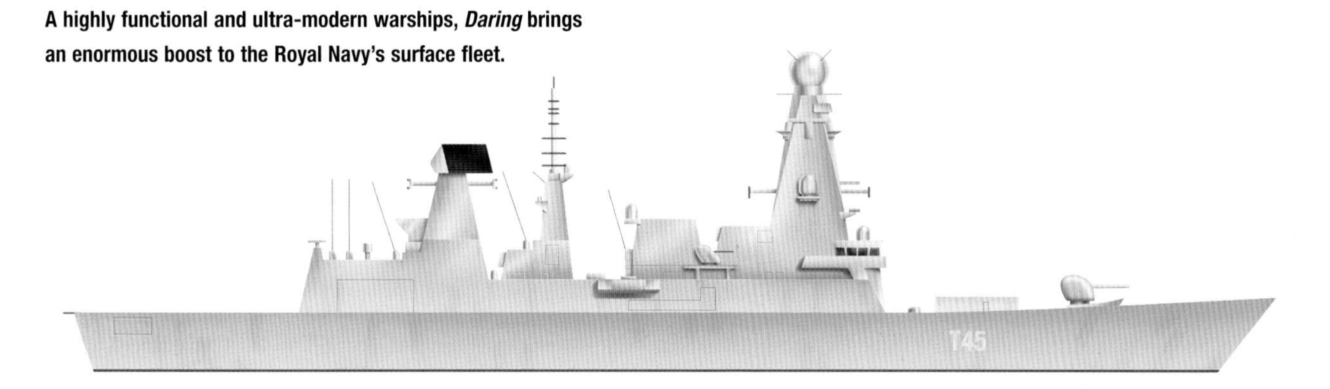

HMS Prince of Wales

HMS *Prince of Wales* is one of two new fleet carriers being built for the Royal Navy, the other being HMS *Queen Elizabeth*. They are expected to enter service in 2014 and 2016.

COUNTRY: UK	
TYPE: Aircraft carrier	
LAUNCH DATE: 2012	
CREW: 1500 (including air crew)	
DISPLACEMENT: 65,000 tonnes (71,650 tons)	
DIMENSIONS: Length: 284m (932ft); Beam: 73m (239ft); Draught: 11m (36ft)	
RANGE: 16,095km (10,000 miles)	
ARMAMENT: Lockheed Martin F-35B STOVL strike fighters, Merlin ASW helicopters	
POWERPLANT: 4 x Rolls-Royce Olympus TM3B gas turbines delivering 112,000 shp to two shafts	
PERFORMANCE: 25 knots	

Image of how the new *Prince of Wales* might look travelling at speed, with two F-35 fighters overhead.

The design of the two carriers was still evolving in 2007, but they were expected to have a displacement of 65,000 tonnes, and they will be three times larger than the Royal Navy's Invincible-class carriers. *Prince of Wales* and *Queen Elizabeth* will have a maximum speed of 25 knots, and at 15 knots they will have a range of 16,095km (10,000 miles). The vessels will carry sufficient food, fuel and stores for seven days of operations at sea. The ships' complement will be around 1200 officers and ratings.

Incorporating two islands

The ships are designed to accommodate an air group of 40 combat aircraft, including the Lockheed Martin F-35B Short Take-Off, Vertical Landing (STOVL) Joint Strike Fighter, the EH-101 Merlin helicopter and a new Maritime Surveillance and Control Aircraft (MASC). Instead of a traditional single island, the design of the new carriers incorporates two islands, the forward one for ship control functions and the latter for flying control. The deck has three runways: two shorter runways of approximately 160m (525ft) for the STOVL Joint Strike Fighter and a long runway, approximately 260m (850ft) over the full length of the carrier, for launching heavily loaded aircraft. The deck will have one or two vertical landing pads for the F-35 aircraft towards the stern of the ship.

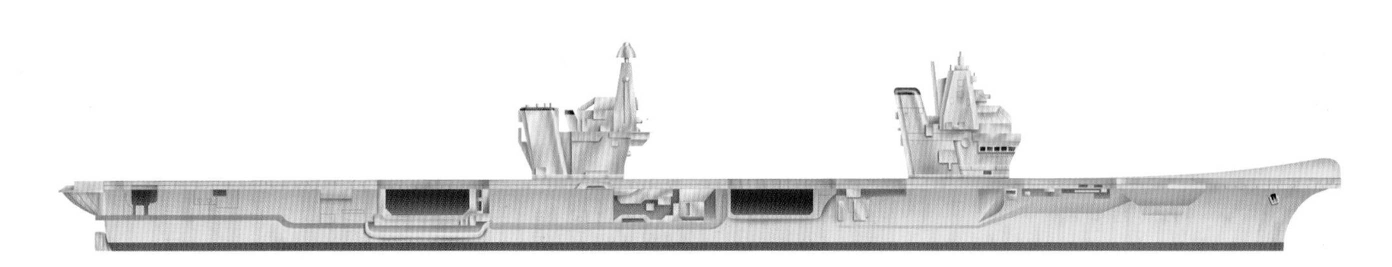

HMS *Prince of Wales* incorporates two islands, each designed to serve different and distinct control functions.

Glossary

AA: Anti-aircraft, as in 'anti-aircraft artillery' (AAA); air-to-air, as in 'air-to-air missile' (AAM).

ASM: Anti-submarine missile; anti-submarine mortar (also air-to-surface missile, air-to-ship/anti-ship missile).

ASW: Anti-submarine warfare.

Axial fire: Gunfire ahead or astern, along the major axis of the vessel.

Battlecruiser: The made-up designation for a hybrid warship armed like a battleship but sacrificing passive protection in the form of armour plate for speed.

Battleship: Originally the biggest and most powerful ships of the fleet, mounting guns of usually 10in (254mm) or larger calibre (the biggest were those of the Japanese Yamato class, which were 18.1 in (460 mm), and heavily armoured. The word was derived from 'line-of-battle ships', the equivalent warships in the days of sailing navies.

Broadside: The simultaneous firing of the guns located on the side (or front) of ship.

Bulkhead/Water-tight bulkhead: A vertical partition employed to divide up a ship's internal space, both longitudinally and transversely. These partitions may be water-tight, in which case the openings in them to allow passage must be capable of being sealed.

Capital ship: A term coined around 1910 to describe the most important naval assets, and group together battleships and battlecruisers (chiefly to give extra credibility to the latter); it was later extended to include monitors.

Carrier battle group: A force designation coined during World War II; it was made up of one or more fleet aircraft carriers together with associated defensive elements – destroyers and cruisers – but often included battleships, which had by then largely been relegated to the shore bombardment role.

Corvette: Originally a (French) sailing ship of war, too small to warrant a rate (and thus the equivalent of the British sloop); more recently, a warship smaller than a frigate or destroyer-escort.

Cruiser: A warship, larger than a frigate or destroyer, much more heavily armed and often armoured to some degree, intended for independent action or to act as a scout for the battlefleet. Modern cruisers operate as defensive elements within carrier battle groups.

CVNX: The latest generation of US Navy aircraft carriers that incorporate many new design features including a new nuclear reactor design (the A1B reactor), stealthier features to help reduce radar profile, electromagnetic catapults, advanced arresting gear, and reduced crewing requirements.

DDG: Guided missile destroyer.

Destroyer: Originally torpedo-boat destroyer; a small warship of little more than 200 tons displacement, itself equipped to launch torpedoes, but also armed with light guns. By the end of Word War I, the first major conflict in which they played a serious role, they had grown to well over 1000 tons, and by the end of World War II, to more than triple that. In more modern times, the type has largely disappeared, and been replaced by enlarged frigates.

Draught (also Draft): The measure of the depth of water required to float a ship, or how much she 'draws'.

Dreadnought: The generic name given to a battleship modelled after *HMS Dreadnought*, the first with all-big-gun armament.

Flotilla: In the Royal Navy up to World War II, an organised unit of (usually eight) smaller warships – destroyers and submarines in particular, but also minesweepers and fast attack craft; cruisers and capital ships were grouped into squadrons, and squadrons and flotillas made up fleets – derived from the diminutive of the Spanish flota, fleet.

Forecastle: Originally the superstructure erected at the bows of a ship to serve as a fighting platform, later the (raised) forward portion and the space beneath it, customarily used as crews' living quarters. Pronounced fo'c'sle.

Frigate: Originally, fifth- or sixth rate ships carrying their guns on a single deck, employed as scouts, and the counterpart of the later cruiser. The term fell into disuse from the mid-1800s and was revived a century later to designate a small warship, between corvette and destroyer in size, used for convoy escort duties; later it became the generic term for smaller warships.

Horsepower: A measure of the power produced by an engine; one horsepower = 550 foot/pounds per second ('the power required to raise 550 pounds through one foot in one second'). Various forms were and are used – brake horsepower (bhp) is the useable power delivered by an engine or motor as measured by a brake on its output shaft.

Keel: The main longitudinal timber of a ship or boat, effectively her spine and certainly her strongest member.

Knot: Internationally, the measure of a ship's speed – one nautical mile per hour.

Minesweeper: A small ship, roughly the size of a trawler (many were, in fact, converted fishing boats originally) adapted and equipped to locate and neutralize submarine mines. Later supplemented by specialist minehunters.

Nautical mile: Internationally, the measure of distance at sea which has become standardised at 6080 ft (1852 m).

Squadron: In the Royal Navy, originally an organised unit of (usually eight) major warships – cruisers and capital ships, but in the US Navy (and the practice became widespread), an organised unit of ships of any type, from minesweepers upwards, the term having taken over from flotilla.

Tonnage: The load carrying capacity of a merchant ship or the displacement of a warship. In a merchant ship, tonnage (the term comes from 'tun' – a wine cask – the original standard cargo unit; 'ton' means not 2240lbs, but 100 cubic feet) may be calculated in a number of ways. Gross tonnage is the total internal volume of a ship's hull derived from a calculation based on her dimensions; net tonnage is the internal volume available for the loading of cargo (ie, the gross tonnage minus space allocated to crew accommodation, machinery, bunkerage etc). Deadweight tonnage is a measurement of the total weight of cargo, fuel and stores a vessel can carry when fully loaded.

Index